Contents

Unit 7 Plants

REPRODUCIBLE STUDENT PAGES

TEACHER SUPPORT AND PLANNING 151

To the Teacher

This unit-based booklet contains resource materials to help you teach this unit more effectively. You will find in chapter order:

Reproducible Pages

Hands-on Activities

MiniLab and BioLab Worksheets: Each activity in this book is an expanded version of each BioLab or MiniLab that appears in the Student Edition of *Biology: The Dynamics of Life*. All materials lists, procedures, and questions are repeated so that students can read and complete a lab in most cases without having a textbook on the lab table. Data tables are enlarged so that students can record data in them. All lab questions are reprinted with lines on which students can write their answers. In addition, for student safety, all appropriate safety symbols and caution statements have been reproduced on these expanded pages. Answer pages for each MiniLab and BioLab are included in the Teacher Support and Planning section at the back of this book.

Real World BioApplications: These two-page activities provide students with the opportunity to explore a technological or everyday application of biology. Each activity is directly related to a major concept in the Student Edition, and several examine principles from the physical sciences that underlie the biology content. While some activities are more hands-on, all require critical thinking and creativity. The teaching notes in the Teacher Support and Planning section at the back of this book suggest chapters and topics with which to correlate the activities, explain the purpose of each activity, offer materials tips and teaching strategies, and provide answers to all questions on the student pages.

Extension and Intervention

Reinforcement and Study Guide in English and Spanish: These pages help students understand, organize, and compare the main biology concepts in the textbook. The questions and activities also help build strong study and reading skills. There are four study guide pages for each chapter and two pages for the BioDigest. Students will find these pages easy to follow because the section titles match those in the textbook. Italicized sentences in the study guide direct students to the related topics in the text.

The *Reinforcement and Study Guide* exercises employ a variety of formats including short-answer questions, multiple-choice, matching, true/false, ordering, labeling, completion, and short essay. The clear, easy-to-follow exercises and the self-pacing format are geared to build your students' confidence in understanding biology. The English pages are followed immediately by the study guide pages in Spanish.

Concept Mapping: The *Concept Mapping* worksheets reinforce and extend the graphic organizational skills introduced in the Skill Handbook in the Student Edition of *Biology: The Dynamics of Life*. Concept maps are visual representations of relationships among particular concepts. By using these worksheets, students will gain experience with three different types of concept maps: the *network tree*, which shows causal information, group hierarchies, and branching procedures; the *events chain*, which describes the stages of a process, the steps in a linear procedure, or a sequence of events; and the *cycle map*, which shows how a series of events interacts to produce a set of results again and again.

There is one *Concept Mapping* worksheet for each chapter in the Student Edition. Each worksheet is geared toward a specific section or sections in the chapter so that you can assign it at the most relevant time. An entire section may be mapped or just a few key

Glencoe Science

BIOLOGY

The Dynamics of Life

Unit 7 Resources
Plants

Mc Graw Hill Glencoe

New York, New York   Columbus, Ohio   Chicago, Illinois   Peoria, Illinois   Woodland Hills, California

A GLENCOE PROGRAM

BIOLOGY: THE DYNAMICS OF LIFE

Glencoe Online
SCIENCE

Visit the Glencoe Science Web site
bdol.glencoe.com

You'll find:
Standardized Test Practice, Interactive
Tutor, Section and Chapter Self-Check
Quizzes, Online Student Edition, Web
Links, Microscopy Links, WebQuest
Projects, Internet BioLabs, In the News,
Textbook Updates, Teacher Bulletin
Board, Teaching Today

and much more!

 **Glencoe**

The **McGraw·Hill** Companies

Send all inquiries to:
Glencoe/McGraw-Hill
8787 Orion Place
Columbus, OH 43240-4027

ISBN 0-07-860218-1

Printed in the United States of America.

3 4 5 6 7 8 9 10 009 08 07 06 05

concepts from the section. Answers to all *Concept Mapping* worksheets are provided in the Teacher Support and Planning section at the back of this book.

Critical Thinking/Problem Solving: For each chapter of ***Biology: The Dynamics of Life,*** a one-page *Critical Thinking* or *Problem Solving* worksheet is provided to extend the material in the Student Edition. Each worksheet is geared to a specific section or sections in the chapter so that you can assign it at the most relevant time. Answers to all worksheets are provided in the Teacher Support and Planning section at the back of this book.

The worksheets follow Bloom's taxonomy of problem solving. Each worksheet tests the students' abilities on one or more of the following areas:

• to use knowledge

• to comprehend what that knowledge means

• to apply that knowledge to a new but related situation

• to analyze the different aspects of new information

• to synthesize new information in order to respond to a particular situation in a creative and logical way

Transparency Activity Masters

Section Focus Transparencies: A *Section Focus Transparency* is provided for every section in the Student Edition. Each transparency contains two questions related to the transparency image. In addition, each transparency is reproduced as a master in this book. These masters are designed to generate interest and focus students' attention on the topic being presented in that section. Teaching strategies background information, and possible answers to the questions for each transparency in this unit can be found in the Teacher Support and Planning section at the back of this book.

Basic Concepts Transparencies: This book contains a blackline master version of each color *Basic Concepts Transparency* for this unit. In most cases, the transparency illustration is different than the illustration in the textbook, providing optimum support for your visual learners. The accompanying worksheet for each transparency master focuses students' attention on the topic, requiring them to analyze the illustration and relate it to the concepts being taught in the textbook. The use of the masters makes the worksheets convenient homework assignments.

Teaching strategies as well as worksheet answers are provided for each transparency. Several transparencies utilize overlays for maximum teaching benefit, and explanations of how to use these overlays are included in the teaching suggestions in the Teacher Support and Planning section at the back of this book.

Reteaching Skills Transparencies: This book contains a blackline master version of each color *Reteaching Skills Transparency* for this unit. The transparencies and masters provide visual tools for reteaching important concepts. To make your reteaching more powerful, the transparencies and masters are developed around basic skills. These skills include, but are not limited to, interpreting scientific illustrations, sequencing, recognizing cause and effect, comparing and contrasting, observing and inferring, and classifying.

The accompanying worksheet for each transparency master focuses students' attention on the topic skill. Students may find it helpful to take notes on the master and use it as a study tool for the chapter. Teaching strategies as well as worksheet answers are provided for each transparency. Several transparencies utilize overlays for maximum teaching benefit, and explanations of how to use these overlays are included in the teaching suggestions in the Teacher Support and Planning section at the back of this book.

Assessment

Chapter Assessment: These worksheets provide materials to assess your students' understanding of concepts from each chapter in this unit. Each chapter test includes several sections that assess students' understanding at different levels.

The *Reviewing Vocabulary* section tests students' knowledge of the chapter's vocabulary. A variety of formats is used, including matching, multiple-choice, and completion.

The *Understanding Main Ideas* section consists of two parts. Part A tests recall and basic understanding of facts presented in the chapter. Part B is designed to be more challenging and requires deeper comprehension of concepts than does Part A. Students may be asked to explain biological processes and relationships or to make comparisons and generalizations.

The *Thinking Critically* section requires students to use several high-order learning skills. For some questions, students will need to interpret data and discover relationships presented in graphs and tables. Other questions may require them to apply their understanding of concepts to solve problems, to compare and contrast situations, and to make inferences or predictions.

In the final section, *Applying Scientific Methods*, students are put into the role of researcher. They may be asked to read about an experiment, simulation, or model, and then apply their understanding of chapter concepts and scientific methods to analyze and explain the procedure and results. Many of the questions in this section are open-ended, giving students the opportunity to demonstrate both reasoning and creative skills. This section, as well as the other sections of each test, begins on a separate page, so that if you wish to omit a section from a test, you can easily do so.

Answers or possible responses to all questions for the chapters in this unit are provided in the Teacher Support and Planning section at the back of this book.

Student Recording Sheet: *Student Recording Sheets* allow students to use the Chapter Assessments in the Student Edition as a practice for standardized testing, giving them an opportunity to use bubble answer grids and number grids for recording answers. There is a recording sheet for each chapter in this unit and a recording sheet for the Unit Assessment at the end of the BioDigest for this unit. Answers for the *Student Recording Sheets* can be found in the side wrap of the Teacher Wraparound Edition on the Chapter Assessment and Unit Review pages.

Teacher Support and Planning

Foldables™ Study Organizer: These pages provide an additional Foldables strategy for each chapter in this unit. The strategy is presented at the top of the page along with more challenging options or suggestions for students who prefer their Foldables to be more creative or informative. The bottom of the page provides instructions for how to make Foldables and can be reproduced and distributed to students who may benefit from the illustrated instructions.

Teacher Guide and Answers: Answers or possible answers for questions in this booklet can be found in chapter order in this section. Materials, teaching strategies, and content background along with chapter references are found where appropriate.

Contents

Chapter 21   What is a plant?

MiniLab 21.1

Applying Concepts

Examining Land Plants

Liverworts are considered to be one of the simplest of all land plants. They show many of the adaptations that other land plants have evolved that enable them to survive on a land environment.

Procedure 🥽 🧤 ☣ 👋

1 Examine a living or preserved sample of Marchantia. **CAUTION:** *Wear disposable latex gloves when handling preserved materials.*

2 Note and record the following observations. Is the plant unicellular or multicellular? Does it have a top and bottom? How do these differ? Is it one cell in thickness or many cells thick? Does the plant seem to grow upright like a tree or is it flat to the ground?

3 Use a dissecting microscope to examine its top and bottom surfaces. Are tiny holes or pores present? If you answer "yes," which surface has pores?

Analysis

1. How might having a multicellular, thick body be an advantage to life on land?

_____

_____

2. Are any structures present that resemble roots? How might they help a land plant?

_____

_____

_____

3. What might be the role of any pores observed on the plant? Why is the location of the pores critical to surviving on a land environment?

_____

_____

_____

MiniLab 21.2

Looking at Modern and Fossil Plants

Comparing and Contrasting

Many modern-day plants have relatives that are known only from the fossil record. Are modern-day plants similar to their fossil relatives? Are there any differences?

Procedure

1 Examine a preserved or living sample of *Lycopodium*, a club moss. **CAUTION:** *Wear disposable latex gloves when handling preserved material.*

2 Note and record the following observations:
   a. Does the plant grow flat or upright like a tree?
   b. Describe the appearance of its leaves and its stem.
   c. Measure the plant's height and diameter in centimeters.

3 Diagram A on page 566 of your text is a representation of a fossil relative called *Lepidodendron*. Record the same observations (a–c).

4 Repeat steps a–c only this time use a preserved or living sample of *Equisetum*, a horsetail. Compare it to Diagram B on page 566 of your text, a representation of a fossil relative called *Calamites*.

Analysis

1. Describe the similarities and differences between *Lycopodium* and *Lepidodendron*. Do your observations justify their closeness as relatives? Explain.

_____

_____

_____

_____

_____

_____

2. Describe the similarities and differences between *Equisetum* and *Calamites*. Do your observations justify their closeness as relatives? Explain.

_____

_____

_____

_____

_____

_____

_____

How can you make a key for identifying conifers?

Chapter **21**

Problem

What kinds of characteristics can be used to create a key for identifying different kinds of conifers?

Hypotheses

State your hypothesis according to the kinds of characteristics you think will best serve to distinguish among several conifer groups. Explain your reasoning.

Objectives

In this BioLab, you will:
- **Compare** structures of several different conifer specimens.

- **Identify** which characteristics can be used to distinguish one conifer from another.
- **Communicate** to others the distinguishing features of different conifers.

Possible Materials

twigs, branches, and cones from several different conifers that have been identified for you

Safety Precautions 🔬 🥽 🧤

Always wash your hands after handling biological materials. Always wear goggles in the lab.

Skill Handbook

Use the **Skill Handbook** if you need additional help with this lab.

1. Make a list of characteristics that could be included in your key. You might consider using shape, color, size, habitat, or other factors.
2. Determine which of those characteristics would be most helpful in classifying your conifers.
3. Determine in what order the characteristics should appear in your key.
4. Decide how to describe each characteristic.

Check the Plan

1. The traits described at each fork in a key are often pairs of contrasting characteristics. For example, the first fork in a key to

conifers might compare "needles grouped in bundles" with "needles attached singly."
2. Someone who is not familiar with conifer identification should be able to use your key to correctly identify any conifer it includes.
3. *Make sure your teacher has approved your experimental plan before you proceed further.*
4. Carry out your plan by creating your key.
5. **Cleanup and Disposal** Return all conifer specimens to the location specified by your teacher for reuse by other students. Wash your hands thoroughly.

How can you make a key for identifying conifers?, *continued*

ANALYZE AND CONCLUDE

1. **Checking Your Hypothesis** Have someone outside your lab group try using your key to identify your conifer specimens. If they are unable to make it work, try to determine where the problem is and make improvements.

2. **Relating Concepts** Give one or more examples of situations in which a key would be a useful tool.

_____

_____

_____

_____

_____

3. **Error Analysis** Is there only one correct way to design a key for your specimens? Explain why or why not.

_____

_____

_____

_____

_____

Chapter 21 What is a plant?

In your textbook, read about the origins and adaptations of plants.

For each answer given below, write an appropriate question.

1. **Answer:** Multicellular eukaryotes having thick cell walls made of cellulose, a protective, waterproof covering, and that can produce its own food in the form of glucose through photosynthesis

   Question: _____

2. **Answer:** The earliest known plant fossils

   Question: _____

3. **Answer:** Protective, waxy layers that cover most fruits, leaves, and stems

   Question: _____

4. **Answer:** The organ of a plant that usually traps light energy for photosynthesis, and is supported by a stem

   Question: _____

5. **Answer:** The organ that anchors a plant, and usually absorbs water and minerals

   Question: _____

In your textbook, read about alternation of generations.

Use each of the terms below just once to complete the passage.

diploid   generations   meiosis
gametes   haploid   sporophyte

The lives of all plants consist of two alternating stages, or **(6)** _____ . The

gametophyte generation of a plant is responsible for the development of **(7)** _____ .

All cells of the gametophyte, including the gametes, are **(8)** _____ . The

(9) _____ generation is responsible for the production of spores. All cells of the

sporophyte are **(10)** _____ . The spores are produced by the sporophyte plant by

(11) _____ and are, therefore, haploid.

In your textbook, read about the origin and adaptations of plants.

Circle the letter of the choice that best completes the statement.

12. The lives of _____ plants include two generations that alternate.
   a. non-seed producing   **b.** seed
   c. all   **d.** most

13. The generation of a plant responsible for producing gametes is the
   a. alternation of generations.   **b.** gametophyte generation.
   c. sporophyte generation.   **d.** seed-producing generation.

14. Gametophyte spores are _____ and sporophyte tissue cells are _____ .
   a. haploid/diploid.   **b.** diploid/haploid.
   c. haploid/haploid.   **d.** diploid/diploid.

15. Non-seed plants _____ that grow into gametophytes.
   a. release spores into the environment   **b.** retain spores in the parent plant
   c. release seeds into the environment   **d.** retain seeds in the parent plant

Answer the following questions.

16. What is the difference between vascular and nonvascular plants?

_____

_____

_____

_____

17. Some land plants produce seeds. What is their function? How do they differ from spores?

_____

_____

_____

_____

18. How do algae and land plants take in substances?

_____

_____

_____

_____

Chapter 21   What is a plant?, *continued*

Reinforcement and Study Guide

Section 21.2 Survey of the Plant Kingdom

In your textbook, read about non-seed plants.

For each item in Column A, write the letter of the matching item in Column B.

Column A	Column B
_____ **1.** Leaves that are found on ferns	**a.** leafy liverworts
_____ **2.** Scaly structures that support male or female reproductive structures	**b.** thallose liverworts
_____ **3.** Plants with a broad, flattened body that resembles a lobed leaf	**c.** fronds
_____ **4.** Plants with three flattened rows of thin leaves	**d.** hornworts
_____ **5.** Nonvascular plants that grow in damp, shady habitats and whose sporophytes resemble horns	**e.** cones

Complete the chart below by marking the appropriate columns for each division of plants.

Division	Vascular	Nonvascular	Non-seed Plants	Seeds in Fruits	Seeds not in Fruits
6. Hepaticophyta					
7. Anthocerophyta					
8. Bryophyta					
9. Psilophyta					
10. Lycophyta					
11. Arthrophyta					
12. Pterophyta					
13. Cycadophyta					
14. Gnetophyta					
15. Ginkgophyta					
16. Coniferophyta					
17. Anthophyta					

Section 21.2 Survey of the Plant Kingdom

In your textbook, read about non-seed plants.

For each answer given below, write an appropriate question.

18. **Answer:** Vascular plants that have neither roots nor leaves

Question: _____

19. **Answer:** Vascular plants that have hollow, jointed stems surrounded by whorls of scalelike leaves, whose cells contain large deposits of silica

Question: _____

20. **Answer:** Plants that may be the ancestors of all plants

Question: _____

21. **Answer:** Hard-walled reproductive cells found in non-seed plants

Question: _____

22. **Answer:** Nonvascular plants that rely on osmosis and diffusion to transport water and nutrients, although some members have elongated cells that conduct water and sugars

Question: _____

In your textbook, read about seed plants.

Use each of the terms below just once to complete the passage.

anthophyta   cycadophyta   gnetophyta
coniferophyta   ginkgophyta

Seed plants are classified into five divisions. Plants from the **(23)** _____ division are palmlike trees with scaly trunks and are often mistaken for ferns or small palm trees. There is only one living species in the **(24)** _____ division. The members of the **(25)** _____ division are the largest, most diverse group of seed plants on Earth and are commonly known as the flowering plants. Three distinct genera make up the plant division called **(26)** _____ . Species of the **(27)** _____ division can be identified by the characteristics of their needlelike or scaly leaves.

Capítulo
21 **¿Qué es una planta?** *Sección 21.1 Adaptación a la vida en la tierra*

En tu libro de texto, lee acerca del origen y las adaptaciones de las plantas.

Escribe la pregunta apropiada para cada respuesta.

1. Respuesta: Eucariotas multicelulares con una gruesa pared celular hecha de celulosa, una cubierta protectora impermeable y que pueden producir su propio alimento en forma de glucosa, mediante la fotosíntesis.

Pregunta: _____

2. Respuesta: Los fósiles más antiguos de plantas.

Pregunta: _____

3. Respuesta: Cubierta protectora cerosa que cubre la mayoría de los frutos, hojas y tallos.

Pregunta: _____

4. Respuesta: El órgano de la planta que por lo general atrapa la energía de la luz para realizar la fotosíntesis y que está sostenido por el tallo.

Pregunta: _____

5. Respuesta: Órgano de la planta que la fija al suelo y que por lo general absorbe agua y minerales.

Pregunta: _____

En tu libro de texto, lee sobre la alternancia de generaciones.

Completa el párrafo usando cada término una sola vez.

| diploide | generaciones | meiosis |
| gametos | haploides | esporofito |

La vida de las plantas consta de dos etapas o **(6)** _____ alternas. La generación

gametofita de una planta se encarga de la producción de **(7)** _____ . Todas las

células del gametofito, incluyendo los gametos, son **(8)** _____ . La generación

(9) _____ se encarga de la producción de esporas. Todas las células del

esporofito son **(10)** _____ . El esporofito de las plantas produce las esporas

mediante **(11)** _____ los que son, por lo tanto, haploides.

En tu libro de texto, lee sobre el origen y las adaptaciones de las plantas.

Haz un círculo alrededor de la letra de la opción que completa mejor cada enunciado.

12. La vida de _____ tiene dos generaciones que se alternan.
   a. las plantas sin semillas   **b.** las plantas con semillas
   c. todas las plantas   **d.** la mayoría de las plantas

13. La generación de la planta que se encarga de la producción de gametos es la
   a. alternancia de generaciones.   **b.** generación gametofita.
   c. generación esporofita.   **d.** generación productora de semillas.

14. Las esporas gametofitas son _____ y las células de los tejidos del esporofito son _____ .
   a. haploides/diploides   **b.** diploides/haploides
   c. haploides/haploides   **d.** diploides/diploides

15. Las plantas sin semillas _____ que posteriormente se convertirán en el gametofito.
   a. liberan esporas en el ambiente   **b.** retienen las esporas en la planta progenitora
   c. liberan semillas en el ambiente   **d.** retienen las semillas en la planta progenitora

Constesta las siguientes preguntas.

16. ¿Cuál es la diferencia entre las plantas vasculares y las plantas no vasculares?

_____

_____

_____

17. Algunas plantas terrestres producen semillas. ¿Cuál es su función? ¿En qué se diferencian de las esporas?

_____

_____

_____

18. ¿Cómo absorben sustancias las algas y las plantas terrestres?

_____

_____

_____

En tu libro de texto, lee acerca de las plantas sin semillas.

Anota la letra de la columna B que corresponda a cada enunciado de la columna A.

Columna A	Columna B
_____ **1.** Las hojas de los helechos	**a.** hepáticas foliosas
_____ **2.** Estructuras escamosas que sostienen los órganos reproductores masculinos o femeninos	**b.** hepáticas talosas
_____ **3.** Plantas de cuerpo amplio y plano que parecen una hoja lobulada	**c.** helechos
_____ **4.** Plantas con tres hileras de hojas delgadas y planas	**d.** ceratófilos
_____ **5.** Plantas no vasculares que crecen en hábitats húmedos y sombreados y cuyos esporofitos parecen un cuerno	**e.** conos

Completa la tabla indicando la columna correcta para cada división de plantas.

División	Vascular	No vascular	Plantas sin semilla	Semillas en frutas	Sin semillas en frutos
6. Hepatofita					
7. Antocerofita					
8. Briofita					
9. Psilofita					
10. Licofita					
11. Artrofita					
12. Pterofita					
13. Cicadofita					
14. Gnetofita					
15. Gingkofita					
16. Coniferofita					
17. Antofita					

Sección 21.2 Visión panorámica del reino vegetal

En tu libro de texto, lee sobre las plantas sin semilla.

Escribe la pregunta apropiada para cada pregunta.

18. Respuesta: Son plantas vasculares que no tienen hojas ni raíces.

Pregunta: _____

19. Respuesta: Son plantas vasculares con tallos huecos y articulados, rodeados por anillos de hojas escamosas cuyas células contienen grandes depósitos de sílice.

Pregunta: _____

20. Respuesta: Es probable que estas plantas sean los ancestros de todas las plantas.

Pregunta: _____

21. Respuesta: Células reproductoras rodeadas de una cubierta dura que poseen las plantas sin semilla.

Pregunta: _____

22. Respuesta: Plantas vasculares que dependen de la difusión y la osmosis para el transporte de agua y minerales, aunque algunos miembros tienen células alargadas que conducen agua y azúcares.

Pregunta: _____

En tu libro de texto, lee sobre las plantas con semillas.

Usa los siguientes términos para completar el párrafo.

antofita	**cicadofita**	**gnetofita**
coniferofita	**gingkofita**	

Las plantas con semilla se clasifican en cinco divisiones. Las plantas de la división **(23)** _____

son árboles que semejan palmas, con troncos escamosos y a menudo se confunden con helechos o palmas

pequeñas. Actualmente, existe una sola especie viva perteneciente a la división **(24)** _____ . Los

miembros de **(25)** _____ forman la división de plantas con semilla de mayor diversidad y

mayor tamaño en el planeta y se conocen como plantas con flores. La división **(26)** _____ .

consta de sólo tres géneros. Las especies de la división **(27)** _____ se clasifican de acuerdo

con las características de sus hojas escamosas o en forma de aguja.

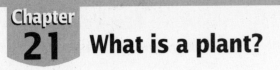

Chapter 21 What is a plant?

Concept Mapping

Use with Chapter 21, Section 21.1

Adaptations of Land Plants

Make a concept map on the adaptations that land plants have for living on land. Include structure and function in the map. Use these words or phrases once: *root, cuticle, stem, seed, leaf.*

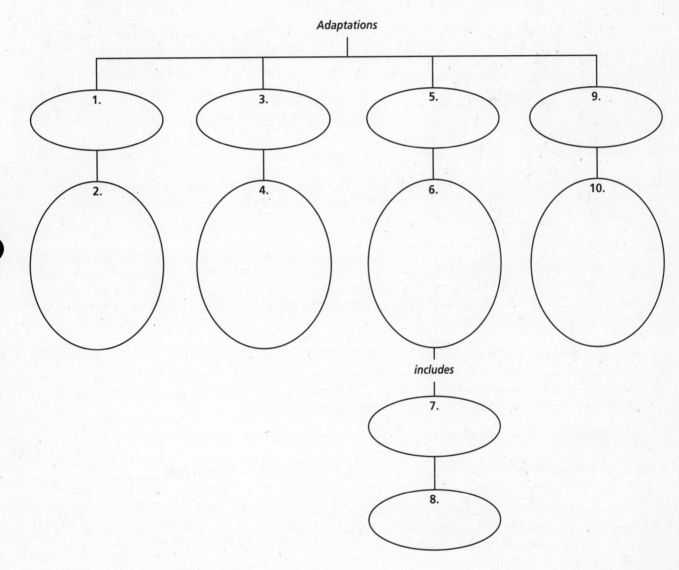

Problem Solving

Use with Chapter 21, Sections 21.1, 21.2

Solving Plant Problems

Suppose that you work part-time at a nearby nursery. You talk with customers who have plant questions. Use your textbook and your knowledge of plants to answer these customers' questions.

1. A man and woman come in carrying a book with a picture of a cypress tree in it: "We were thinking about getting this type of tree for our neighbor. Her birthday's coming up soon. What kind of flowers does it produce?"

_____

_____

2. Two young boys come in holding a plastic bag containing a small, decaying piece of wood covered with a mat of moss: "We were walking in the park and found this plant growing on a stick. What plant is this? Can we grow it in our house?"

_____

_____

3. A man comes in holding what appears to be a moss. It has three rows of thin leaves attached to a stem. The leaves are flattened. He wants to know what kind of moss it is.

_____

_____

_____

4. A girl comes in with her biology textbook. She points to an illustrated geologic time scale in the book: "My teacher said that these big plants called club mosses found in Paleozoic forests still grow today. I don't remember ever seeing a plant like this. Do they exist?"

_____

_____

_____

Section Focus

Master 50 Life on Land

Use with Chapter 21, Section 21.1

❶ How would you describe the environment in which these plants live?

❷ What are some adaptations that help plants live in this type of environment?

Master 51 **Bryophytes and Hepaticophytes**

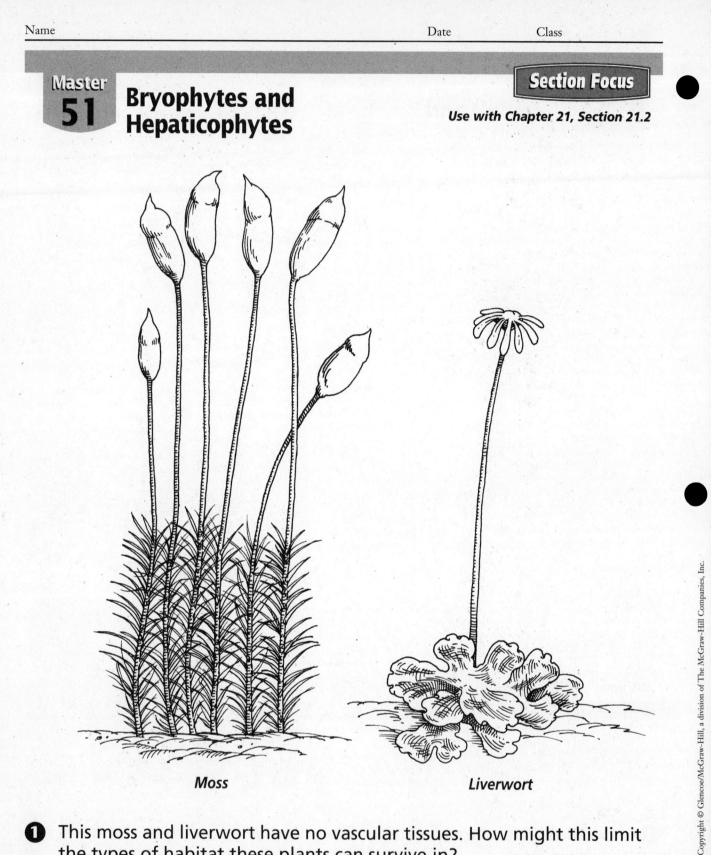

Moss   *Liverwort*

❶ This moss and liverwort have no vascular tissues. How might this limit the types of habitat these plants can survive in?

❷ How else might the lack of vascular tissue limit these plants?

Master 33

Phylogeny of Non-Seed Plants

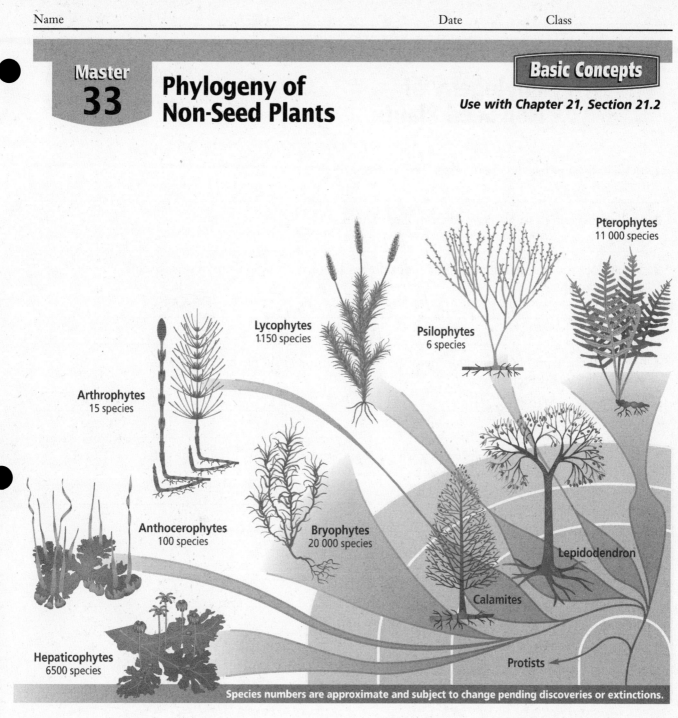

Pterophytes
11 000 species

Lycophytes
1.150 species

Psilophytes
6 species

Arthrophytes
15 species

Anthocerophytes
100 species

Bryophytes
20 000 species

Lepidodendron

Calamites

Protists

Hepaticophytes
6500 species

Species numbers are approximate and subject to change pending discoveries or extinctions.

Worksheet 33 Phylogeny of Non-Seed Plants

Use with Chapter 21, Section 21.2

1. Which division has the greatest number of species?

_____

2. Which division of plants evolved from the calamites?

_____

3. What does the transparency suggest about the evolutionary relationship of protists and non-seed plants?

_____

_____

4. What are the common names for members of the divisions Psilophyta, Lycophyta, Arthrophyta, and Pterophyta?

_____

_____

5. All but three of the plant divisions shown possess vascular tissue. What are the three divisions of nonvascular plants?

_____

_____

6. Use the transparency to describe the history of lycophytes.

_____

_____

_____

_____

Chapter
21 **What Is a Plant?**

Reviewing Vocabulary

Match the definition in Column A with the term in Column B.

Column A	Column B
_____ **1.** A plant organ that absorbs water and dissolved minerals usually from the soil	**a.** cone
_____ **2.** Contains tissues of tubelike, elongated cells through which water, food, and other materials are transported	**b.** frond
_____ **3.** Provides structural support for growth and contains tissues for transporting materials from one part of the plant to another	**c.** cuticle
_____ **4.** Scaly structure that supports male or female reproductive structures	**d.** leaf
_____ **5.** Plant organ that contains an embryo along with a food supply and is covered by a protective coat	**e.** root
_____ **6.** Protective, waxy layer covering most leaves and stems	**f.** vascular plant
_____ **7.** Leaflike structure of ferns that can vary in length from 1 cm to 500 cm	**g.** stem
_____ **8.** A plant organ that grows from a stem and is usually where photosynthesis occurs	**h.** seed

Write a definition for each term listed below.

9. nonvascular plant

_____

_____

_____

10. vascular tissues

_____

_____

_____

Chapter Assessment

Understanding Concepts (Part A)

Complete the three tables by using the following list of words and phrases:

club mosses	mosses
ferns	needlelike or scaly leaves
flowering plants	only one living species
hornworts	palmlike trees with cones as long as 1 m
horsetails	three distinct genera
liverworts	whisk ferns

Phylogeny of Plants (based on division)

Non-seed nonvascular plant divisions

Division	Common Name
Hepaticophyta	a.
Anthocerophyta	b.
Bryophytes	c.

Non-seed, vascular plant division

Division	Common Name
Psilophyta	d.
Lycophyta	e.
Arthrophyta	f.
Pterophyta	g.

Seed Plants

Division	Common characteristics
Cycadophyta	h.
Gnetophyta	i.
Ginkgophyta	j.
Coniferophyta	k.
Anthophyta	l.

Understanding Concepts (Part B)

Answer the following questions.

1. Why do scientists think that plants probably evolved from green algae?

_____

_____

_____

_____

2. In what ways does vascular tissue provide an adaptive advantage for plants?

_____

_____

_____

_____

3. How does the cuticle prevent water loss?

_____

_____

_____

4. What major events highlight the evolution of plants?

_____

_____

_____

5. Compare the location of seeds of cycads, conifers, and flowering plants.

_____

_____

_____

_____

Chapter 21 **What Is a Plant?,** *continued*

Thinking Critically

Use the graph to answer questions 1–3.

1. Investigators study the influence of light on spore germination in bryophytes. A spore has germinated when a small, green filament of cells is just protruding through the ruptured spore coat. Based on the graph, what wavelength of light appears to initiate spore germination?

_____

_____

_____

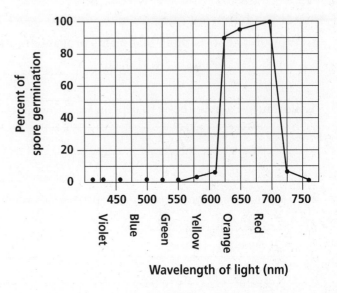

2. What is the optimum wavelength for spore germination?

_____

_____

3. What colors of light favor spore germination?

_____

Answer the following questions.

4. Aquatic bryophytes have been invaluable in monitoring pollution by heavy metals in contaminated water. However, the highest concentrations in the water do not always correspond to the highest values in the plants. Why might this be?

_____

_____

_____

_____

5. Some mosses that live in deserts dry out, and all their metabolic activities cease during a dry spell. At the next rainfall, however, they revive, grow, and reproduce. Why is this behavior adaptive?

_____

_____

_____

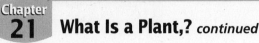

Applying Scientific Methods

In an effort to understand alternation of generations in bryophytes, scientists have tried in the laboratory to develop moss sporophytes from gametophytes *without fertilization*. When filaments of cells that develop into haploid gametophytes were cultivated in a sugar-free medium, only gametophytes were produced. However, when botanists transferred these cell filaments to a medium supplemented with 2 percent sucrose, the filaments produced a large number of sporophyte sporangia.

1. Formulate a hypothesis to explain why a medium with 2 percent sucrose causes this change in the reproductive cycle. (Be creative in your thinking.)

_____

_____

_____

_____

_____

2. Plan an experiment to prove your hypothesis.

_____

_____

_____

_____

3. What will be your variable in this experiment?

_____

_____

4. What will be your control?

_____

_____

5. Some experimenters showed that the effect of sucrose is enhanced when lower light intensities are also present. How might less light affect the experiment?

_____

_____

_____

Chapter Assessment

Applying Scientific Methods   *continued*

6. Scientists also discovered that after about 12 weeks of producing sporophytes, the plants stopped reproducing. However, if the gametophytes were transferred to a new sucrose medium, they began the formation of sporophytes again. In a medium lacking sucrose, the plants produced only gameto-phytes. How might these results be explained?

_____

_____

_____

_____

_____

7. Why would botanists perform an experiment like this, which seems to involve events that do not usu-ally occur in nature?

_____

_____

_____

_____

_____

Assessment
Student Recording Sheet

Use with pages 574–575 of the Student Edition

Vocabulary Review

Write the vocabulary words that match the definitions in your book.

1. _____   4. _____

2. _____   5. _____

3. _____

Understanding Key Concepts

Select the best answer from the choices given and fill in the corresponding oval.

6. Ⓐ Ⓑ Ⓒ Ⓓ   10. Ⓐ Ⓑ Ⓒ Ⓓ

7. Ⓐ Ⓑ Ⓒ Ⓓ   11. Ⓐ Ⓑ Ⓒ Ⓓ

8. Ⓐ Ⓑ Ⓒ Ⓓ   12. Ⓐ Ⓑ Ⓒ Ⓓ

9. Ⓐ Ⓑ Ⓒ Ⓓ

Constructed Response

Record your answers for Questions 13–15 on a separate sheet of paper.

Thinking Critically

16.   Fill in the correct terms to complete the concept map.

1. _____   4. _____

2. _____   5. _____

3. _____

17.   **REAL WORLD BIOCHALLENGE** Follow your teacher's instructions for presenting your BioChallenge answer.

Chapter
21 **Assessment**
Student Recording Sheet, (continued)

Chapter Assessment

*Use with pages 574–575
of the Student Edition*

Standardized Test Practice

The Princeton Review

Part 1 Multiple Choice

Select the best answer from the choices given and fill in the corresponding oval.

18. Ⓐ Ⓑ Ⓒ Ⓓ   21. Ⓐ Ⓑ Ⓒ Ⓓ

19. Ⓐ Ⓑ Ⓒ Ⓓ   22. Ⓐ Ⓑ Ⓒ Ⓓ

20. Ⓐ Ⓑ Ⓒ Ⓓ

Part 2 Constructed Response/Grid In

Record and bubble in your answer on the grid.

23.

24. Record your answer for Question 24 on a separate sheet of paper.

Contents

Chapter 22 The Diversity of Plants

MiniLab 22.1

Experimenting

Identifying Fern Sporangia

When you admire a fern growing in a garden or forest, you are admiring the plant's sporophyte generation. Upon further examination, you should be able to see evidence of spores being formed. Typically, the evidence you are looking for can be found on the underside of the ferns' fronds.

Procedure

1 Place a drop of water and a drop of glycerin at opposite ends of a glass slide.

2 Use forceps to gently pick off one sorus from a frond. Place it in the drop of water and add a coverslip.

3 Add a second sorus to the glycerin and add a coverslip.

4 Observe both preparations under low-power magnification and note any similarities and differences. Look for large sporangia (resembling heads on a stalk) and spores (tiny round bodies released from a sporangium). **CAUTION:** *Use caution when working with a microscope, microscope slides, and coverslips.*

Analysis

1. How does the appearance of spores in water and in glycerin differ?

_____

2. What did the glycerin do to the sporangium?

_____

_____

3. Form a hypothesis that may explain how sporangia naturally burst.

_____

_____

4. Form a hypothesis that may explain how sporangia were affected by glycerin.

_____

_____

MiniLab 22.2

Comparing and Contrasting

Comparing Seed Types

Anthophytes are classified into two classes, the monocotyledons (monocots) and dicotyledons (dicots) based on the number of seed leaves.

Procedure

1 Use the data table below.

2 Examine the variety of seeds given to you. Use forceps to gently remove the seed coat or covering from each seed if one is present.

3 Determine the number of cotyledons present. If two cotyledons are present, the seed will easily separate into two equal halves. If one cotyledon is present, it will not separate into halves. Record your observations in the data table.

4 Add a drop of iodine to each seed. Note the color change. **CAUTION: *Wash your hands with soap and water after handling chemicals*.** Record your observations in the data table.

Data Table

Seed Name	Number of Cotyledons	Monocot or Dicot	Color with Iodine
Lima bean			
Rice			
Pea			
Rye			

Analysis

1. Starch turns purple when iodine is added to it. Describe the color change when iodine was added to each seed.

_____

2. Hypothesize why seeds contain stored starch.

_____

_____

Copyright © Glencoe/McGraw-Hill, a division of The McGraw-Hill Companies, Inc.

Researching Trees on the Internet

PREPARATION

Problem
Use the Internet to find different trees that would be suitable for planting in your community.

Objectives
In this BioLab, you will:
- **Research** the characteristics of five different trees.
- **Use the Internet** to collect and compare data from other students.

- **Conclude** which trees would be most suitable for planting in your community.

Materials
Internet access

Skill Handbook
Use the **Skill Handbook** if you need additional help with this lab.

PROCEDURE

1. Use the data table.
2. Pick five tree species that you wish to research. Note: Your teacher may provide you with suggestions if necessary.
3. Visit **bdol.glencoe.com/internet_lab** to find links to information needed for this BioLab.
4. Record the information in your data table.

Data Table

	1	2	3	4	5
Tree Name (common name)					
Scientific Name					
Division					
Soil/Water Preference					
Temperature Tolerance					
Height at Maturity					
Rate of Growth					
General Shape					
Disease/Pests					
Special Care					
Deciduous or evergreen					
Additional Information					

Researching Trees on the Internet, *continued*

ANALYZE AND CONCLUDE

1. **Define Operationally** Explain the difference between trees classified as either Coniferophyta or Anthophyta.

_____

_____

2. **Analyze** Was the information provided on the Internet helpful in completing your data table? Explain your answer.

_____

_____

3. **Think Critically** What do you consider to be the most important characteristic when deciding on the most suitable tree for your community? Explain your answer.

_____

_____

4. **Use the Internet** Using the information you gathered from the Internet, which tree species would most likely be the:

   a. most suitable along a street in your community? Explain your answer.

_____

_____

   b. least suitable along a street in your community? Explain your answer.

_____

_____

5. **Apply** Explain why tree selections would differ if your community were located in:

   a. a desert biome

_____

_____

   b. a tiaga biome

_____

_____

   c. a tropical rain forest biome

_____

_____

Chapter 22 The Diversity of Plants

In your textbook, read about nonvascular plant divisions—bryophyta, hepaticophyta, and anthocerophyta.

Complete each statement.

1. Nonvascular plants are successful in habitats with adequate _____ .

2. The _____ generation is dominant in nonvascular plants.

3. Sperm are produced in male reproductive structures called _____ , and eggs are produced in female reproductive structures called _____ .

4. Mosses have colorless multicellular structures called _____ , which help anchor the stem to the soil.

5. Most liverworts have _____ that helps reduce evaporation of water from the plant's tissues.

6. Liverworts occur in many environments and include two groups: the _____ liverworts and the _____ liverworts.

7. One unique feature of hornworts is the presence of one to several _____ in each cell.

8. The common names for the nonvascular plants in bryophyta, hepaticophyta, and anthocerophyta are _____ , _____ , and _____ .

Circle the letter of the response that best completes the statement.

9. Nonvascular plants are not as common or as widespread as vascular plants because
   a. nonvascular plants are small.
   b. the life functions of nonvascular plants require a close association with water.
   c. nonvascular plants are limited to dry habitats.
   d. none of the above.

10. The life cycle of nonvascular plants includes an alternation of generations between a
    a. diploid sporophyte and a diploid gametophyte.
    b. haploid sporophyte and a haploid gametophyte.
    c. diploid sporophyte and a haploid gametophyte.
    d. haploid sporophyte and a diploid gametophyte.

11. Fossil and genetic evidence suggests that the first land plants were
    a. mosses.   c. liverworts.
    b. sphagnum moss.   d. hornworts.

Reinforcement and Study Guide

Section 22.2 Non-Seed Vascular Plants

In your textbook, read about the alternation of generations of non-seed vascular plants and lycophyta.

Use each of the terms below just once to complete the passage.

antheridia	leaves	sporophyte
archegonia	prothallus	strobilus
egg	reproductive cells	zygote
fertilization	sperm	

Unlike nonvascular plants, the spore-producing **(1)** _____ is the dominant generation

in vascular plants. A major advance in vascular plants was the adaptation of **(2)** _____ to

form structures that protect the developing **(3)** _____ . In some non-seed vascular

plants, spore-bearing leaves form a compact cluster called a(n) **(4)** _____. Spores are

released from this compact cluster. These spores then grow to form the gametophyte, called a(n)

(5) _____ . This structure is relatively small and lives in or on soil. The prothallus then

forms **(6)** _____ , male reproductive structures, and **(7)** _____ , female

reproductive structures. **(8)** _____ are released from an antheridium and swim through a

film of water to the **(9)** _____ in an archegonium. **(10)** _____ occurs and

a large, dominant sporophyte plant develops from the **(11)** _____ .

For each statement below, write true or false.

_____ **12.** The leafy stems of lycophytes resemble clubs, and their reproductive structures are moss shaped.

_____ **13.** The leaves of lycophytes occur as pairs, whorls, or spirals along the stem.

_____ **14.** Lycophytes are simple vascular plants with creeping leaves.

_____ **15.** The club moss is commonly called ground pine because it is evergreen and resembles a miniature pine tree.

In your textbook, read about arthrophyta and pterophyta.

Complete each statement.

16. The hollow-stemmed horsetail appears to be jointed with scalelike _____ surrounding each joint.

17. The most recognized generation of ferns is the _____ generation.

18. The _____ in most ferns is a thin, flat structure.

19. In most ferns, the main stem, called a _____ , is underground. It contains many starch-filled cells for _____ .

20. The leaves of a fern are called _____ and grow upward from the rhizome.

21. Fronds are often divided into _____ , which are attached to a central rachis.

22. Ferns were the first vascular plants to evolve leaves with branching _____ of vascular ranchis.

23. The common names for the seedless vascular plants, lycophyta, arthrophyta, and pterophyta are

_____ , _____ , and _____ .

Answer the following questions on the lines provided.

24. Why are arthrophytes, or horsetails, sometimes referred to as scouring rushes?

_____

_____

_____

25. Why might you be more familiar with ferns than with club mosses and horsetails?

_____

_____

_____

_____

Chapter 22 The Diversity of Plants, *continued*

In your textbook, read about the seed plants—cycadophyta, gingkophyta, gnetophyta, coniferophyta, and anthophyta.

Complete each statement.

1. An _____ , or young diploid sporophyte, has food-storage organs called _____.

2. Vascular plants that produce _____ in cones are sometimes called _____ .

3. Seed plants do not require _____ for _____ .

4. The male gametophyte develops inside a structure called a(n) _____ that includes sperm cells, nutrients, and a protective outer covering.

5. The female gametophyte, which produces the egg cell, is contained within a sporophyte structure called a(n) _____ .

6. Biennials develop large storage organs and live for _____ .

7. Perennials produce flowers and seeds periodically for _____ .

8. Annual plants live for _____ .

9. _____ have one seed leaf; _____ have two seed leaves.

For each statement below, write <u>true</u> or <u>false</u>.

_____ **10.** Cycads are related to palm trees but their leaves unfurl like fern fronds.

_____ **11.** There is only one species of ginkgo tree alive today.

_____ **12.** Most gnetophytes today are found in the deserts or mountains of Africa, Asia, North America, and Central and South America.

_____ **13.** Most conifers are evergreen plants that lose their needlelike leaves all at once and only grow in nutrient-rich soil.

_____ **14.** Dropping leaves is an adaptation in deciduous plants to reduce water loss when it is less available, such as during winter.

_____ **15.** Anthophytes are unique in that they are the only division of plants that produce fruits.

En tu libro de texto, lee sobre las divisiones de plantas no vasculares—briofitas, hepaticofitas y antocerofitas.

Completa cada enunciado.

1. Las plantas no vasculares sólo pueden sobrevivir en hábitats con una cantidad adecuada de

   _____ .

2. La generación _____ es dominante en las plantas no vasculares.

3. Los espermatozoides se producen en estructuras reproductoras masculinas llamadas

   _____ , mientras que los óvulos se producen en estructuras reproductoras femeninas

   llamadas _____ .

4. Los musgos tienen estructuras multicelulares sin color llamadas _____ , que les

   permiten fijarse al suelo.

5. La mayoría de las hepáticas tienen _____ que les ayuda a reducir la

   evaporación de agua de los tejidos de las plantas.

6. Las hepáticas habitan una gran variedad de ambientes y se dividen en dos grupos: las hepáticas

   _____ y las hepáticas _____ .

7. Una característica única de las psilofitas es la presencia de un(a) a varios(as)

   _____ en cada célula.

8. Los nombres comunes de las plantas no vasculares: briofita, hepaticofita y antocerofita son

   _____ , _____ y _____ .

Haz un círculo alrededor de la letra de la opción que completa mejor cada enunciado.

9. Las plantas no vasculares no son tan comunes ni están tan ampliamente distribuidas como las plantas
   vasculares porque
   a. las plantas no vasculares son pequeñas.
   b. las funciones vitales de las plantas no vasculares requieren la cercanía al agua.
   c. las plantas no vasculares sólo viven en hábitats secos.
   d. ninguna de las anteriores.

10. El ciclo de vida de las plantas no vasculares incluye la alternancia de generaciones entre
    a. un esporofito diploide y un gametofito diploide.
    b. un esporofito haploide y un gametofito haploide.
    c. un esporofito diploide y un gametofito haploide.
    d. un esporofito haploide y un gametofito diploide.

11. Los fósiles y las pruebas genéticas sugieren que las primeras plantas terrestres fueron
    a. los musgos.   **c.** las hepáticas.
    b. los musgos esfagnáceos.   **d.** los ceratófilos.

En tu libro de texto, lee sobre la alternancia de generaciones en las plantas vasculares sin semillas y en las licofitas.

Completa el párrafo usando los siguientes términos.

anteridio	hojas	esporofito
arquegonio	prótalo	estróbilo
óvulo	células reproductoras	cigoto
fecundación	espermatozoides	

A diferencia de las plantas no vasculares, el **(1)** _____ , la generación productora de

esporas es la generación dominante en las plantas vasculares. Una de las principales ventajas de las plantas

vasculares fue la adaptación de las **(2)** _____ para formar estructuras de protección de

los(las) **(3)** _____ . En algunas plantas vasculares sin semilla, las hojas que contienen las

esporas forman un racimo compacto llamado **(4)** _____ , que es el sitio donde se liberan

las esporas. Al crecer, las esporas se convierten en el gametofito conocido como **(5)** _____ .

Esta estructura es relativamente pequeña y vive bajo o sobre el suelo. El prótalo se convierte en el

(6) _____ , o estructura reproductora masculina y en el

(7) _____ o estructura reproductora femenina. Los **(8)** _____ son liberados

desde el anteridio y nadan a través de una delgada capa de agua hacia los **(9)** _____ ,

localizados en el arquegonio. Después de que ocurre la **(10)** _____ , se forma la planta

esporofítica dominante a partir del **(11)** _____ .

Indica si cada uno de los enunciados es <u>verdadero</u> o <u>falso</u>.

_____ **12.** Los tallos foliosos de las licofitas semejan garrotes y sus estructuras reproductoras
             parecen musgos.

_____ **13.** Las hojas de las licofitas ocurren en pares, en anillos o en espirales alrededor del tallo.

_____ **14.** Las licofitas son plantas vasculares simples con hojas rastreras.

_____ **15.** Los licopodios también se conocen como pinillos porque son siempreverdes y porque
             parecen un pino en miniatura.

La diversidad de las plantas,
continuación

Sección 22.2 Las plantas vasculares sin semilla

En tu libro de texto, lee sobre las artrofitas y las pterofitas.

Completa cada enunciado.

16. El tallo hueco de los equisetos parece tener nudos con _____ en forma de escama alrededor de cada nudo.

17. La generación más visible de los helechos es la generación _____ .

18. El _____ de la mayoría de los helechos es una estructura delgada y plana.

19. En la mayoría de los helechos el tallo principal, llamado _____ , es subterráneo. El tallo contiene muchas células ricas en almidones que sirven como _____ .

20. Las hojas del helecho se llaman _____ y crecen verticalmente a partir del rizoma.

21. Las frondas a menudo se dividen en _____ , unidas a un raquis central.

22. Los helechos fueron las primeras plantas en desarrollar hojas con _____ ramificadas de tejido vascular.

23. Los nombres comunes de las plantas vasculares sin semilla de la división licofita, artrofita y pterofita son _____ , _____ y _____ .

Contesta las siguientes preguntas.

24. ¿Por qué en inglés, a veces a las artrofitas o equisetos se les dice colas de caballo?

_____

_____

25. ¿Por qué es probable que estés más familiarizado(a) con los helechos que con los licopodios y los equisetos?

_____

_____

_____

_____

Capítulo 22 La diversidad de las plantas, *continuación*

En tu texto, lee sobre las plantas con semilla—cicadofitas, ginkgofitas, gnetofitas, coniferofitas y antofitas.

Completa cada enunciado.

1. Un(a) _____ , o esporofito diploide joven, tiene órganos de almacenamiento de alimento llamados _____ .

2. Las plantas que producen _____ en conos, también se conocen como _____ .

3. Las plantas con semilla no requieren _____ para que ocurra la _____ .

4. El gametofito masculino se desarrolla dentro de una estructura llamada _____ que incluye los espermatozoides, los nutrientes y una cubierta protectora.

5. Una estructura del esporofito llamada _____ contiene el gametofito femenino, que es la estructura que produce el huevo.

6. Las plantas bienales desarrollan órganos grandes para almacenar alimentos y viven durante _____ .

7. Las plantas perennes producen flores y semillas periódicamente durante _____ .

8. Las plantas anuales viven durante _____ .

9. Las _____ tienen una hoja embrionaria; las _____ tienen dos hojas embrionarias.

Indica si cada uno de los enunciados es <u>verdadero</u> o <u>falso</u>.

_____ 10. Las cicadáceas están relacionadas con los árboles de palma, pero sus hojas se desenrollan como las frondas de un helecho.

_____ 11. Actualmente, sólo existe una especie viva de gingko.

_____ 12. La mayoría de las gnetofitas actuales se hallan en los desiertos o las montañas de África, Asia, Norteamérica, Centroamérica y Suramérica.

_____ 13. La mayoría de las coníferas son siempreverdes que pierden simultáneamente todas sus hojas que tienen forma de aguja y sólo crecen en suelos ricos en nutrientes.

_____ 14. La caída de las hojas es una adaptación en las plantas de hojas caducas para reducir la pérdida de agua cuando hay menos agua disponible, como en el invierno.

_____ 15. Las antofitas se caracterizan por ser la única división de plantas que producen frutos.

Characteristics of Anthophyta

Complete this concept map comparing the characteristics of the two classes of anthophyta. Use these words or phrases once: *monocotyledons, one seed leaf, two seed leaves, dicotyledons, three, parallel veins, four or five, branched veins.*

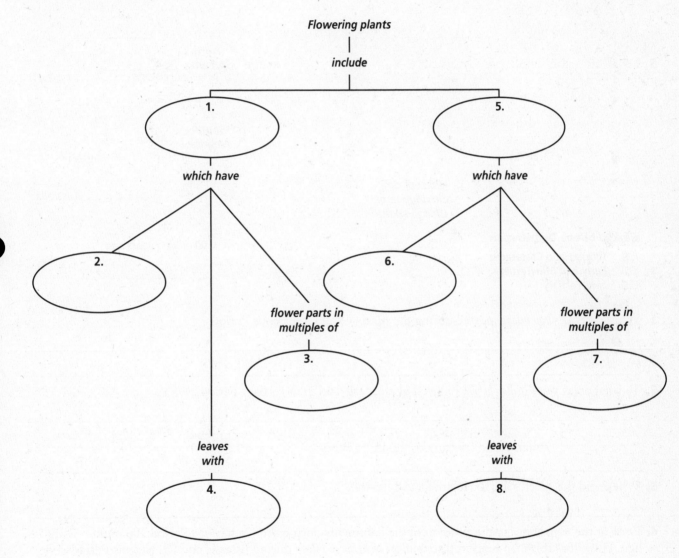

Chapter 22 The Diversity of Plants

Distribution of *Ginkgo Biloba*

The map on the left below shows the past and present natural distribution of *Ginkgo biloba*. The map on the right shows the position of the continents 100 million years ago. Study the maps and answer the questions that follow.

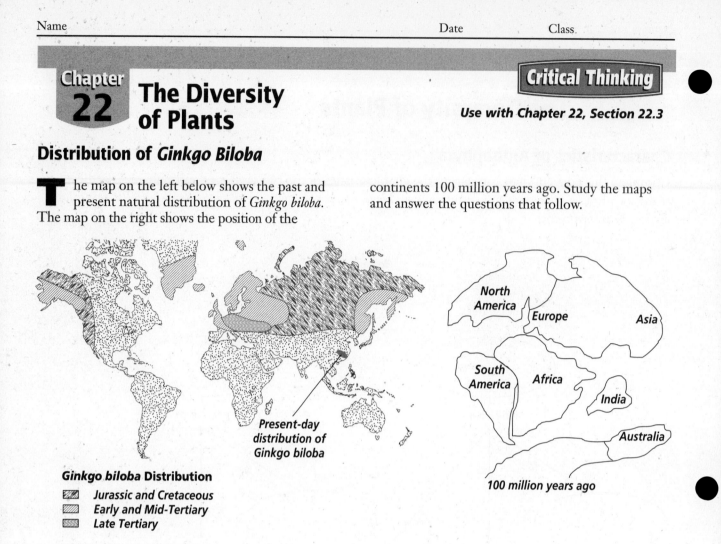

Present-day distribution of Ginkgo biloba

100 million years ago

Ginkgo biloba Distribution

- Jurassic and Cretaceous
- Early and Mid-Tertiary
- Late Tertiary

1. Where was *Ginkgo biloba* located during the Jurassic and Cretaceous Periods?

_____

_____

2. To what areas was *Ginkgo biloba* reduced by the early and mid-Tertiary period?

_____

_____

_____

3. Where did the species live during the late Tertiary?

_____

4. Look at the map showing the position of the continents during the Cretaceous Period 100 million years ago. How does this map support distribution of *Ginkgo biloba* during Jurassic and Cretaceous Periods?

_____

_____

_____

_____

Master 52

What's Green and Essential for Life?

Section Focus

Use with Chapter 22 , Section 22.1

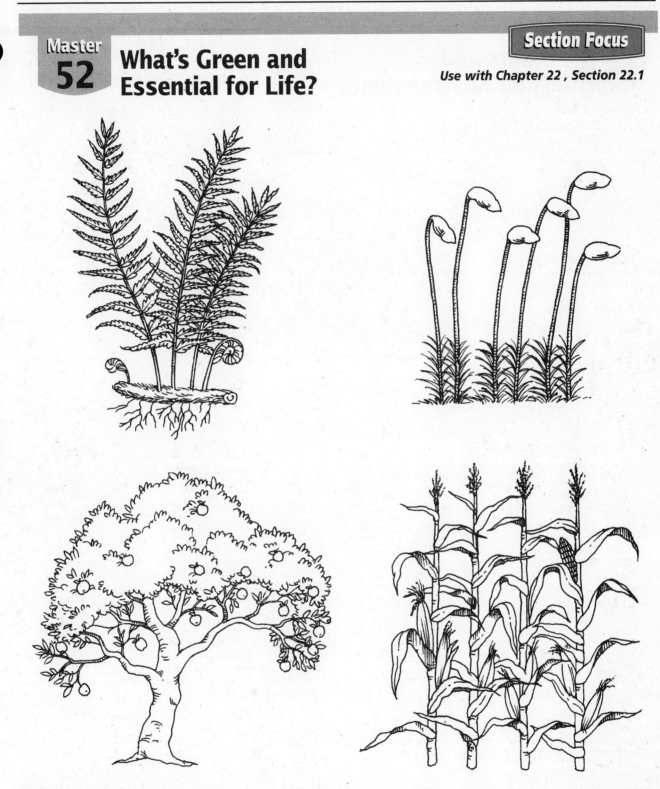

1 Why do you think that plants such as these are essential for most life on Earth?

2 In what major way does the top pair of plants differ from the bottom pair?

Master 53 **Plants and Their Environments**

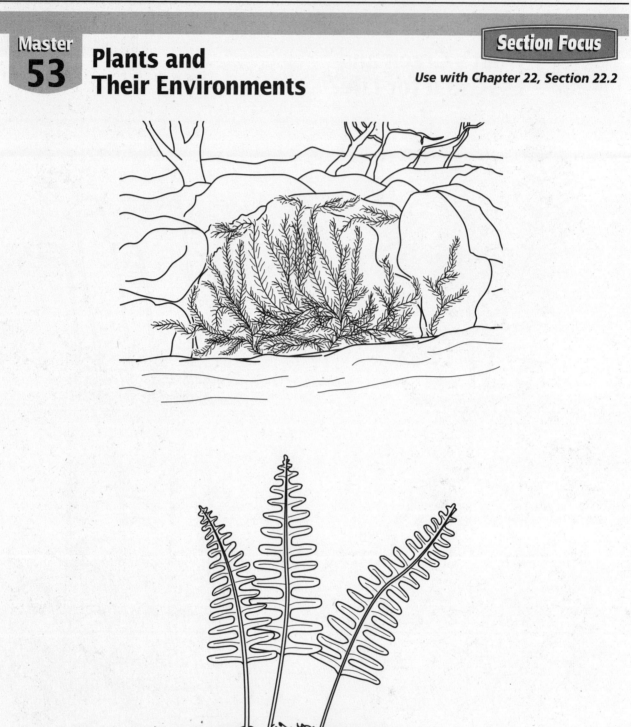

1 What type of environments do these two plants live in?

2 How are the structures of these two plants related to their environments?

Master
54 **Gymnosperm Cones**

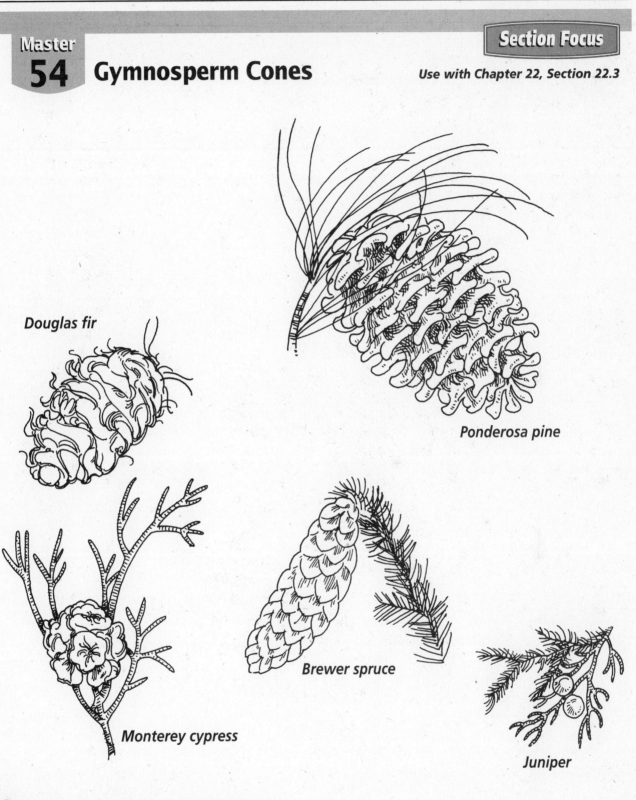

Douglas fir

Ponderosa pine

Monterey cypress

Brewer spruce

Juniper

❶ How are these cones similar?

❷ What is their function?

Master 34

Phylogeny of Seed Plants

Use with Chapter 22, Section 22.3

Basic Concepts

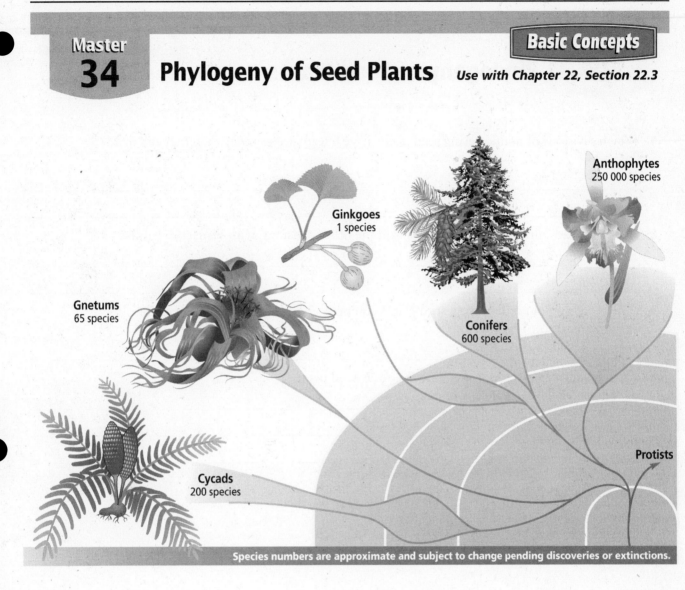

Species numbers are approximate and subject to change pending discoveries or extinctions.

Worksheet 34 **Phylogeny of Seed Plants**   *Basic Concepts*   *Use with Chapter 22, Section 22.3*

1. Which divisions of nonflowering seed plants have fewer species today than they did in the past?

_____

_____

2. How do cycads differ from the organisms of the other divisions, with respect to habitat?

_____

_____

3. Which division of nonflowering seed plants comprises most of the population of the evergreen forests of North America?

_____

4. What advantages do seed plants have over non-seed plants?

_____

_____

_____

Master 35

Phylogeny of Flowering Plants

Basic Concepts

Use with Chapter 22, Section 22.3

Kingdom Plantae
Division Anthophyta
Classes: Dicotyledones
          Monocotyledones
About 250 000 species

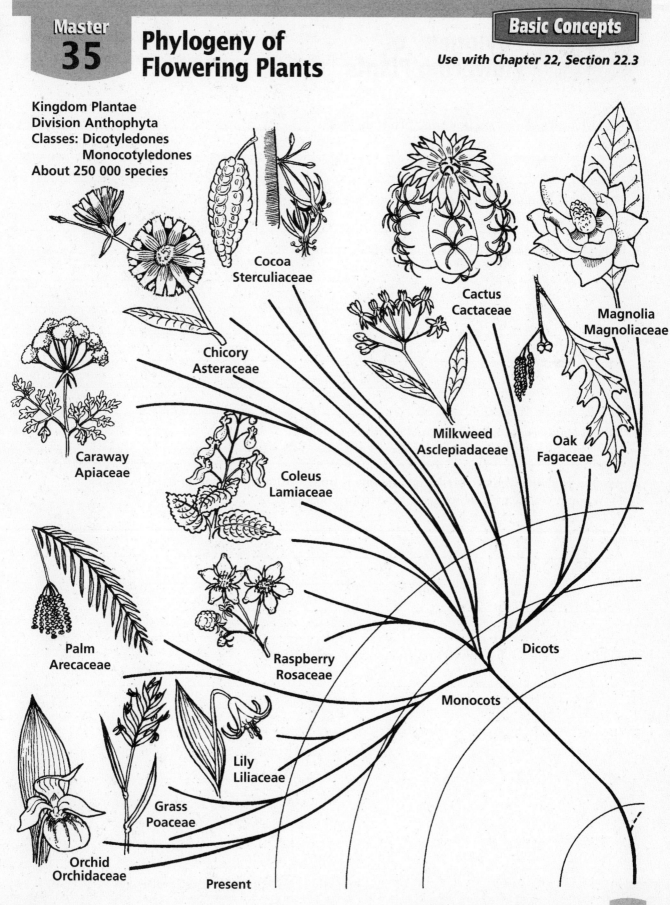

Cocoa
Sterculiaceae

Cactus
Cactaceae

Magnolia
Magnoliaceae

Chicory
Asteraceae

Milkweed
Asclepiadaceae

Oak
Fagaceae

Caraway
Apiaceae

Coleus
Lamiaceae

Palm
Arecaceae

Raspberry
Rosaceae

Dicots

Monocots

Lily
Liliaceae

Grass
Poaceae

Orchid
Orchidaceae

Present

Worksheet 35 **Phylogeny of Flowering Plants**

Basic Concepts

Use with Chapter 22, Section 22.3

1. Into what two classes are flowering plants divided?

_____

_____

2. How many families of monocots are shown in the phylogenetic diagram?

_____

3. What foods come from monocot plants? Dicot plants?

_____

_____

_____

_____

_____

4. Which family is most closely related to Apiaceae?

_____

5. Assume you are given two seeds and told one is from a palm and the other from a cactus. How could you identify which seed came from which plant?

_____

_____

_____

_____

_____

6. Which class probably evolved first—monocots or dicots?

_____

Reviewing Vocabulary

Match the definition in Column A with the term in Column B.

Column A

_____ **1.** Cluster of sporangia

_____ **2.** Leaf of a fern

_____ **3.** A plant that loses all its leaves at one time

_____ **4.** Early gametophyte in lycophytes, arthrophytes, and pterophytes

_____ **5.** Organism at an early stage of development

_____ **6.** Thick, underground stem

_____ **7.** Food-storage organ of some plant embryos

_____ **8.** The ripened ovary of a flower

_____ **9.** Structure in which the female gametophyte develops

_____ **10.** Structure that includes sperm nuclei, nutrients, and a protective outer covering

Column B

a. cotyledon

b. embryo

c. deciduous plant

d. frond

e. fruit

f. ovule

g. pollen grain

h. prothallus

i. rhizome

j. sorus

Compare and contrast each pair of terms.

11. antheridium, archegonium

_____

_____

_____

_____

12. annuals, perennials

_____

_____

_____

_____

Understanding Main Ideas (Part A)

In the space at the left, write the letter of the word or phrase that best completes the statement or answers the question.

_____ **1.** Horsetails are

    a. bryophytes.   **b.** arthrophytes.   **c.** lycophytes.   **d.** pterophytes.

_____ **2.** You can recognize that a plant is a dicotyledon if it has

    a. parallel veins.   **b.** branched veins.

    c. one seed leaf within the seed.   **d.** flower parts in multiples of three.

_____ **3.** *Sphagnum*, or peat moss, which is used in the horticultural industry, is a(n)

    a. bryophyte.   **b.** hepaticophyte.   **c.** anthocerophyte.   **d.** lycophyte.

_____ **4.** In the fern life cycle, a spore germinates to form a(n)

    a. thallus.   **b.** antheridium.   **c.** prothallus.   **d.** archegonium.

_____ **5.** Which of the following divisions do *not* include nonvascular plants?

    a. Bryophyta   **b.** Hepaticophyta   **c.** Anthocerophyta   **d.** Anthophyta

_____ **6.** In most seed plants, fertilization does not require

    a. a film of water to carry the sperm to the egg.

    b. alternation of generations.

    c. the production of eggs.

    d. a gametophyte generation.

_____ **7.** Which of these are vascular plants?

    a. club mosses   **b.** spike mosses   **c.** ferns   **d.** all of these

_____ **8.** The fronds of some ferns are divided into

    a. rhizomes.   **b.** pinnae.   **c.** cycads.   **d.** sori.

_____ **9.** Which of the following is *not* a characteristic of a non-seed vascular plant?

    a. These plants exhibit alternation of generations.

    b. The gametophyte generation is dominant.

    c. They have vascular tissues through which water and sugars are transported.

    d. Plants are found in a variety of habitats.

_____ **10.** Most conifers

    a. lose all their leaves when water is unavailable.

    b. lose no water through the leaves.

    c. are deciduous trees.

    d. never lose all their leaves at one time.

Chapter 22 The Diversity of Plants, *continued*

Understanding Main Ideas (Part B)

Answer the following questions.

1. Describe the major characteristics of nonvascular plants.

_____

_____

_____

2. What advantages does a seed plant have over a non-seed plant?

_____

_____

_____

_____

_____

_____

3. What are the advantages of fruit-enclosed seeds?

_____

_____

_____

_____

_____

4. What advantages does an evergreen tree have?

_____

_____

_____

_____

_____

_____

Chapter 22 The Diversity of Plants, *continued*

Thinking Critically

Refer to the graph to answer questions 1 and 2.

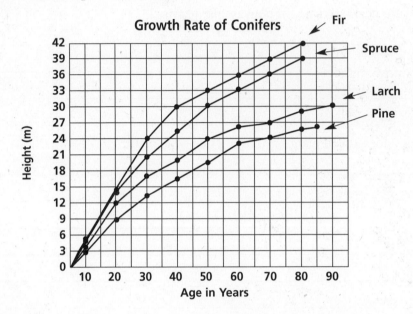

1. In the table, write the correct information about the patterns of growth of certain conifers.

	Age at maximum growth		Maximum height		Height at 45 years
Fir	_____	Fir	_____	Fir	_____
Spruce	_____	Spruce	_____	Spruce	_____
Larch	_____	Larch	_____	Larch	_____
Pine	_____	Pine	_____	Pine	_____

2. How does the graph show that these conifers grow according to their own growth pattern?

_____

_____

_____

3. The ginkgo, with its broad leaves that turn yellow in autumn, looks more like a flowering plant than a gymnosperm. Why is the ginkgo classified as a gymnosperm?

_____

_____

Applying Scientific Methods

Bracken ferns are one of the most widely distributed species of ferns. Brackens occur in all but hot and cold desert regions of the world. In many regions, this species invades the grasslands, where it becomes a troublesome weed that is difficult to eradicate because of its persistent underground rhizome. The problem is worsened because bracken is a poisonous plant. It causes thyamine deficiency, which results in the death of certain animals.

1. What circumstances might arise in your community such that you might need to find out how to control the growth of brackens?

_____

_____

2. Bracken spores will germinate in lava, mortar of brickwork, abandoned building sites, bomb sites, and fire-damaged natural habitats. However, they will not germinate within a bracken colony. Hypothesize as to what the limiting factor in the germination of bracken spores might be.

_____

_____

_____

_____

3. Plan an experiment to test your hypothesis. Decide the conditions under which you will grow the bracken fern.

_____

_____

_____

_____

4. What will be the variable in this experiment?

_____

_____

_____

_____

Chapter 22 The Diversity of Plants, continued

Applying Scientific Methods *continued*

5. What will be the control?

_____

_____

6. If you found that when bracken spores grew into ferns, the other plant in the pot flourished, what might you conclude?

_____

_____

7. How could you prove that the conclusion you came to in question 6 was correct?

_____

_____

_____

_____

8. If you found that the plant did not flourish or even died when it was grown with bracken spores, what would you conclude?

_____

_____

_____

9. How could you prove that the conclusion you came to in question 8 was correct?

_____

_____

_____

_____

Chapter
22 Assessment
Student Recording Sheet

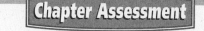
Use with pages 602–603 of the Student Edition

Vocabulary Review

Write the vocabulary words that match the definitions in your book.

1. _____   4. _____

2. _____   5. _____

3. _____

Understanding Key Concepts

Select the best answer from the choices given and fill in the corresponding oval.

6. (A) (B) (C) (D)   10. (A) (B) (C) (D)

7. (A) (B) (C) (D)   11. (A) (B) (C) (D)

8. (A) (B) (C) (D)   12. (A) (B) (C) (D)

9. (A) (B) (C) (D)   13. (A) (B) (C) (D)

Constructed Response

Record your answers for Questions 14 and 15 on a separate sheet of paper.

Thinking Critically

Record your answers for Questions 16 and 17 on a separate sheet of paper.

18. **REAL WORLD BIOCHALLENGE** Follow your teacher's instructions for presenting your BioChallenge answer.

19. Construct your concept map on a separate sheet of paper.

Standardized Test Practice

The Princeton Review

Part 1   Multiple Choice

Select the best answer from the choices given and fill in the corresponding oval.

20. (A) (B) (C) (D)

21. (A) (B) (C) (D)

22. (A) (B) (C) (D)

23. (A) (B) (C) (D)

24. (A) (B) (C) (D)

Part 2
Constructed Response/Grid In

Record your answers for Questions 25 and 26 on a separate sheet of paper.

Chapter 23 Plant Structure and Function

Chapter 23

MiniLab 23.1   Examining Plant Tissues

Observing

Pipes are hollow. Their shape or structure allows them to be used efficiently in transporting water. Plant vascular tissues have this same efficiency in structure.

Procedure

1 Snap a celery stalk in half and remove a small section of "stringy tissue" from its inside.

2 Place the material on a glass slide. Add several drops of water. Place a second glass slide on top. **CAUTION:** *Use caution when working with a microscope and slides.*

3 Press down evenly on the top glass slide with your thumb directly over the plant material.

4 Remove the top glass slide. Add more water if needed. Add a coverslip.

5 Examine the celery material under low- and high-power magnification. Diagram what you see.

6 Repeat steps 2–5 using some of the soft tissue inside the celery stalk.

Analysis

1. Describe the appearance of the stringy tissue inside the celery stalk.

_____

_____

_____

2. Describe the appearance of the soft tissue inside the celery stalk.

_____

_____

_____

3. Does the structure of these tissues suggest their functions?

_____

_____

MiniLab 23.2   Observing Leaves

Comparing and Contrasting

Identifying leaf characteristics can help you identify plants. Use these leaf images to complete this field investigation.

Procedure

CAUTION: *Keep your hands away from your mouth while doing this investigation. Wash your hands thoroughly after you complete your work.*

1 With your teacher's permission, examine leaves on five different plants on your school campus, or observe preserved leaves. Do not use conifers.

2 Sketch a leaf from each plant. Beside each sketch, label the leaf as simple or compound, list its venation, and write the word that describes its arrangement on the stem.

Analysis

1. As a class, place leaves having the same three characteristics into groups. List the characteristics and count the number of leaves in each group. Display class results in a bar graph.

_____

_____

_____

2. Why would a botanist compare and contrast leaf structure?

_____

_____

_____

_____

Determining the Number of Stomata on a Leaf

Chapter 23

PREPARATION

Problem
How can you count the total number of stomata on a leaf?

Objectives
In this BioLab, you will:
- **Measure** the area of a leaf.
- **Observe** the number of stomata seen under a high-power field of view.
- **Calculate** the total number of stomata on a leaf.

Materials
microscope
glass slide
water and dropper
green leaf from an onion plant
single-edged razor blade
ruler
glass cover

Safety Precautions 🔬 🔪 🧤 🥽 🧴
Wear latex gloves when handling an onion.

Skill Handbook
Use the **Skill Handbook** if you need additional help with this lab.

PROCEDURE

1. Use Data Tables 1 and 2.
2. To calculate the area of the high-power field of view for your microscope, go to *Math Skills* in the **Skill Handbook.** Enter the area in Data Table 2.
3. Obtain an onion leaf and carefully cut it open lengthwise using a single-edged razor blade. **CAUTION:** *Be careful when cutting with a razor blade.*
4. Measure the length and width of your onion leaf in millimeters. Record these values in Data Table 2.
5. Remove a small section of leaf and place it on a glass slide with the dark green side facing DOWN.
6. Add several drops of water and gently scrape away all green leaf tissue using a back and forth motion with the razor blade. An almost transparent layer of leaf epidermis will be left on the slide.
7. Add water and a cover glass to the epidermis and observe under low-power magnification. Locate an area where guard cells and stomata can clearly be seen. **CAUTION:** *Use caution when working with a microscope, microscope slides, and coverslips.*

8. Switch to high-power magnification.
9. Count and record the number of stomata in your field of view. Consider this trial 1. Record your count in Data Table 1.

Data Table 1

Trial	Number of stomata
1	
2	
3	
4	
5	
Total	
Average	

10. Move the slide to a different area. Count and record the number of stomata in this field of view. Consider this trial 2.

INVESTIGATE BioLab Determining the Number of Stomata on a Leaf, continued

11. Repeat step 10 for Trials 3, 4, and 5. Calculate the average number of stomata observed in a high-power field of view.

12. Calculate the total number of stomata on the entire onion leaf by following the directions in Data Table 2.

13. **Cleanup and Disposal** Clean all equipment as instructed by your teacher and return everything to its proper place. Dispose of leaf tissue and coverslips properly. Wash your hands thoroughly.

Data Table 2

Area of high-power field of view	= _____ mm²
Length of leaf portion in mm	= _____ mm
Width of leaf portion in mm	= _____ mm
Calculate area of leaf (length × width)	= _____ mm²
Calculate number of high-power fields of view on leaf (area of leaf ÷ the area of one high-power field of view)	= _____
Calculate total number of stomata (number of high-power fields of view × average number of stomata from Data Table 1)	= _____

ANALYZE AND CONCLUDE

1. **Communicate** Compare your data with those of your other classmates. Offer several reasons why your total number of stomata for the leaf may not be identical to your classmates'.

   _____

2. **Predict** Would you expect all plants to have the same number of stomata per high-power field of view? Explain your answer.

   _____

   _____

3. **Comparing and Contrasting** What are the advantages to using sampling techniques? What are some limitations?

   _____

   _____

4. **Error Analysis** Analyze the following steps of this experiment and explain how you can change the procedure to improve the accuracy of your data.
   a. five trials in Data Table 1

   _____

   b. calculating the area of your high-power field of view

   _____

Chapter 23 Plant Structure and Function

In your textbook, read about plant cells and tissues.

Match the definitions in Column 1 with the terms in describes from Column 2. Place the letter from Column 2 in the spaces under Column 1.

Column 1	Column 2
_____ **1.** The most abundant kind of plant cells	**a.** apical meristem
_____ **2.** Long cells with unevenly thickened cell walls. This type of cell wall allows the cells to grow.	**b.** collenchyma
_____ **3.** Cells with walls that are very thick and rigid. At maturity, these cells often die, leaving the cell walls to provide support for the plant.	**c.** companion cell
_____ **4.** Dermal tissue that is composed of flattened parenchyma cells that cover all parts of the plant	**d.** cork cambium
_____ **5.** Openings in the cuticle of the leaf that control the exchange of gases	**e.** epidermis
_____ **6.** Cells that control the opening and closing of the stomata.	**f.** guard cells
_____ **7.** Hairlike projections that extend from the epidermis	**g.** meristem
_____ **8.** Plant tissue composed of tubular cells that transports water and dissolved minerals from the roots to the rest of the plant	**h.** parenchyma
_____ **9.** Tubular cells, with tapered ends, that have cell walls with pits through which water and dissolved minerals flow	**i.** phloem
_____ **10.** Lateral meristem that produces a tough covering for the surface of stems and roots	**j.** sclerenchyma
_____ **11.** Vascular tissue that transport sugars to all parts of the plant	**k.** sieve tube member
_____ **12.** Long, cylindrical cells through which sugars and organic compounds flow	**l.** stomata
_____ **13.** Nucleated cells that help manage the transport of sugars and other organic compounds through the sieve cells of the phloem	**m.** tracheids
_____ **14.** Areas where new cells are produced	**n.** trichomes
_____ **15.** Growth tissue found at or near the tips of roots and stems	**o.** vascular cambium
_____ **16.** Tubular cells that transport water throughout the plant. These cells are wider and shorter than tracheids.	**p.** vessel element
_____ **17.** Lateral meristem that produces new xylem and phloem cells in dicot stems and roots	**q.** xylem

In your textbook, read about roots and stems.

Label the parts of the dicot root. Use these choices:

cortex   phloem   epidermis   endodermis   xylem

Dicot Root

1. _____

2. _____

3. _____

4. _____

5. _____

For each statement below, write <u>true</u> or <u>false</u>.

_____ **6.** A root hair is a small extension of an epidermal, or outermost, cell layer of a dicot root.

_____ **7.** Layers of parenchyma cells make up the cortex of a dicot root and the central pith of a monocot root.

_____ **8.** Outside the endodermis is a tissue called the pericycle that develops vertical roots.

_____ **9.** Vascular cambium cells found near the center of a root produce xylem and phloem cells that increase the diameter of the root.

_____ **10.** Behind the root tip are cell-producing growth tissues called the root cap.

_____ **11.** The difference between roots and stems lies in the way they transport water.

_____ **12.** Primary growth in a stem occurs in the apical meristem.

In your textbook, read about stems and leaves.

Circle the letter of the response that best completes the statement.

13. Many wildflowers with soft, green stems are plants that have
    a. woody stems.   **b.** herbaceous stems.
    c. woody roots.   **d.** all of the above.

14. The functions of a plant's stem include
    a. transporting sugar.   **b.** supporting the plant.
    c. transporting water and minerals.   **d.** all of the above.

15. Any portion of the plant that stores sugars is called a
    a. petiole.   **b.** mesophyll.
    c. root cap.   **d.** sink.

16. The movement of sugars through the phloem is called
    a. photosynthesis.   **b.** transpiration.
    c. translocation.   **d.** food storage.

In your textbook, read about the leaves of a plant.

Use each of the terms below just once to complete the passage.

stomata	extend	cuticle	transpiration	epidermis
veins	stem	petiole	photosynthesis	mesophyll

There are many parts to a leaf. Grass leaves grow right out of the **(17)** _____ ,

but other leaves are connected to the stem by a stalk called the **(18)** _____ .

The petiole is made of vascular tissues that **(19)** _____ up into the leaf to form

(20) _____ .

The outer surface of a leaf has a **(21)** _____ that covers the epidermis.

Inside the epidermis are two layers of photosynthetic cells that make up the

(22) _____ . Cells in the palisade layer have many chloroplasts and

carry out most of the leaf's **(23)** _____ . Leaves have a(n)

(24) _____ with a waxy cuticle and **(25)** _____ help

prevent water loss. The loss of water through stomata is called **(26)** _____ .

Chapter 23 Plant Structure and Function, *continued*

In your textbook, read about plant hormones and plant responses.

Complete each statement.

1. A _____ is a chemical that is produced in one part of an organism and transported to another part, where it causes a physiological change.

2. The group of plant hormones called _____ promote cell elongation. Indoleacetic acid (IAA) is an example of this group of hormones.

3. The group of growth hormones that cause plants to grow taller because, like auxins, they stimulate cell elongation, are called _____ .

4. The hormones called _____ are so named because they stimulate cell division by stimulating the production of proteins needed for mitosis.

5. The plant hormone called _____ is a simple, gaseous compound composed of carbon and hydrogen that speeds the ripening of fruits.

6. A plant's response to an external stimulus that comes from a particular direction is called a _____ .

7. A responsive movement of a plant that is not dependent on the direction of the stimulus is called a _____ .

Determine if the statement is true. If it is not, rewrite the italicized part to make it true.

8. A *large* amount of hormone is needed to make physiological changes in a plant.

_____

9. If gibberellins are applied to the tip of a dwarf plant, it will grow *taller*.

_____

10. The growth of a plant towards light is caused by an unequal distribution of *ethylene* in the plant's stem.

_____

11. If a tropism is *negative*, the plant grows toward the stimulus.

_____

12. The growth of a plant toward light is called *phototropism*.

_____

13. *Gravitropism* is the direction of plant growth in response to gravity.

_____

14. A plant's response to touch is called *cytokinin*.

_____

Copyright © Glencoe/McGraw-Hill, a division of The McGraw-Hill Companies, Inc.

Estructura y función en las plantas

En tu libro de texto, lee sobre las células y los tejidos vegetales.

Anota la letra de la columna 2 que corresponda a cada enunciado de la columna 1. Anota la letra en el espacio indicado.

Columna 1	Columna 2

Columna 1

_____ **1.** El tipo de célula vegetal más abundante.

_____ **2.** Células alargadas con paredes celulares de grosor variable. Este tipo de pared celular permite el crecimiento de las células.

_____ **3.** Células con paredes gruesas y rígidas. Cuando maduran, este tipo de células generalmente están muertas y su pared celular permanece como estructura de soporte de la planta.

_____ **4.** Tejido de las dermis compuesto de células parenquimatosas aplanadas que cubren todas las partes de la planta.

_____ **5.** Apertura en la cutícula de la hoja que controla el intercambio de gases.

_____ **6.** Células que controlan la apertura y el cierre de los estomas.

_____ **7.** Proyecciones en forma de vellosidad que se extienden a partir de la epidermis.

_____ **8.** Tejido de la planta compuesto por células tubulares que transportan agua y minerales disueltos desde la raíz hacia el resto de la planta.

_____ **9.** Células tubulares de extremos afilados y paredes celulares con huecos a través de los cuales fluyen el agua y los minerales disueltos.

_____ **10.** Meristemo lateral que produce la cubierta dura que cubre la superficie de tallos y raíces.

_____ **11.** Tejido vascular que transporta azúcares hacia toda la planta.

_____ **12.** Células cilíndricas y alargadas a través de las cuales fluyen los azúcares y compuestos orgánicos.

_____ **13.** Células nucleadas que ayudan a controlar el transporte de azúcares y otros compuestos orgánicos a través de las células cribosas.

_____ **14.** Áreas donde se producen nuevas células.

_____ **15.** Tejido de crecimiento situado en la punta o cerca de la punta de raíces y tallos.

_____ **16.** Células tubulares que transportan agua a través de la planta. Estas células son más cortas y gruesas que las traqueidas.

_____ **17.** Meristemo lateral que produce nuevas células de xilema y de floema en los tallos y raíces de dicotiledóneas.

Columna 2

a. meristemo apical

b. colénquima

c. célula acompañante

d. cámbium suberígeno

e. epidermis

f. células guardianas

g. meristemo

h. parénquima

i. floema

j. esclerénquima

k. miembros de los tubos cribosos

l. estomas

m. traqueidas

n. tricomas

o. cámbium vascular

p. tráqueas

q. xilema

Capítulo 23 **Estructura y función de las plantas,** *continuación*

Sección 23.2 Raíces, tallos y hojas

En tu libro de texto, lee acerca de raíces y tallos.

Identifica las partes de la raíz de una dicotiledónea. Usa las siguientes opciones:

corteza   floema   epidermis   endodermis   xilema

Raíz de dicotiledónea

1. _____

2. _____

3. _____

4. _____

5. _____

Indica si cada uno de los enunciados es <u>verdadero</u> o <u>falso</u>.

_____ **6.** Los pelos radiculares son una pequeña extensión de la capa epidérmica, o capa más externa, de las células de la raíz de una dicotiledónea.

_____ **7.** Capas de células parenquimatosas forman la corteza de la raíz de una dicotiledónea y la médula de la raíz de una monocotiledónea.

_____ **8.** Fuera de la endodermis, existe un tejido llamado periciclo donde se originan las raíces verticales.

_____ **9.** Las células del cámbium vascular localizadas cerca del centro de una raíz producen más células del floema y del xilema, aumentando el diámetro de la raíz.

_____ **10.** Por detrás del ápice de la raíz hay tejidos de crecimiento que producen células llamadas pilorriza.

_____ **11.** La diferencia entre el tallo y la raíz está en la manera en que transportan agua.

_____ **12.** El crecimiento primario de un tallo ocurre en el meristemo apical.

Estructura y función de las plantas, *continuación*

En tu libro de texto, lee acerca de los tallos y las hojas.

Haz un círculo alrededor de la letra de la opción que completa mejor cada enunciado.

13. La gran variedad de flores silvestres de tallos verdes y suaves son plantas que tienen
    a. tallo leñoso.   **b.** tallo herbáceo.
    c. raíces leñosas.   **d.** todas las anteriores.

14. Las funciones del tallo de la planta incluyen
    a. el transporte de azúcares.   **b.** el sostén de la planta.
    c. el transporte de agua y minerales.   **d.** todas las anteriores.

15. Cualquier parte de la planta que almacena azúcares se conoce como
    a. pecíolo.   **b.** mesófilo.
    c. pilorriza.   **d.** depósito.

16. El movimiento de azúcares a través del floema se conoce como
    a. fotosíntesis.   **b.** transpiración.
    c. translocación.   **d.** almacenamiento de alimentos.

En tu libro de texto, lee sobre las hojas de las plantas.

Usa los siguientes términos para completar el párrafo.

estomas	extienden	cutícula	transpiración	epidermis
venas	tallo	pecíolo	fotosíntesis	mesófilo

Las hojas constan de muchas partes. Las hojas de pasto crecen directamente a partir del

(17) _____ , pero otras hojas están conectadas al tallo mediante un pequeño talluelo

conocido como **(18)** _____ . El pecíolo está formado por tejidos vasculares que se

(19) _____ hacia la hoja para formar las **(20)** _____ .

La superficie exterior de la hoja tiene una **(21)** _____ que cubre la epidermis.

Bajo la epidermis hay dos capas de células fotosintéticas que forman el **(22)** _____ .

Las células en empalizada tienen muchos cloroplastos y realizan la mayor parte de la

(23) _____ de la hoja. Las hojas tienen una **(24)** _____

con una cutícula cerosa y **(25)** _____ que ayudan a prevenir la pérdida de agua. La

pérdida de agua a través de los estomas se conoce como **(26)** _____ .

Estructura y función de las plantas, *continuación*

En tu libro de texto, lee sobre las hormonas vegetales y las reacciones de las plantas.

Completa cada enunciado.

1. Un(a) _____ es una sustancia química producida en una parte del cuerpo y que, al ser transportada hacia otra parte del cuerpo, ocasiona un cambio fisiológico.

2. El grupo de fitohormonas llamado _____ ocasiona la elongación de las células. El ácido indolacético (AIA) es un ejemplo de este grupo de hormonas.

3. El grupo de hormonas de crecimiento que ocasiona un aumento en la altura de las plantas porque, al igual que las auxinas, producen elongación de las células se llaman _____ .

4. Las hormonas llamadas _____ se conocen con este nombre porque estimulan la división celular, al estimular la producción de las proteínas necesarias para la mitosis.

5. La fitohormona llamada _____ es un gas de estructura simple formado por carbono e hidrógeno, el cual acelera la maduración de los frutos.

6. La reacción de una planta a estímulos externos provenientes de una dirección particular se conoce como _____ .

7. La reacción de una planta que no depende de la dirección de donde proviene el estímulo se conoce como _____ .

Si el enunciado es verdadero, escribe *verdadero*; de lo contrario, modifica la sección en itálicas para hacer verdadero el enunciado.

8. Se requieren *grandes* cantidades de una hormona para producir cambios fisiológicos en una planta.

_____

9. Si se le aplican giberelinas en su punta, una planta enana *aumentará* su altura.

_____

10. Una distribución desigual de *etileno* en el tallo de la planta produce el crecimiento en dirección de la luz.

_____

11. Si un tropismo es *negativo*, la planta crecerá en dirección al estímulo.

_____

12. El crecimiento de una planta hacia la luz se conoce como *fototropismo*.

_____

13. El *gravitropismo* es la dirección del crecimiento de la planta en respuesta a la gravedad.

_____

14. La reacción de una planta al tacto se conoce como *citoquinina*.

_____

Chapter
23 Plant Structure and Function *Use with Chapter 23, Section 23.1*

Plant Tissues

Complete the concept map of plant tissues. Use these words or phrases once: *apical meristem, cork cambium, dermal, ground, guard cell, lateral meristem, phloem, root hair, vascular, vascular cambium, xylem.*

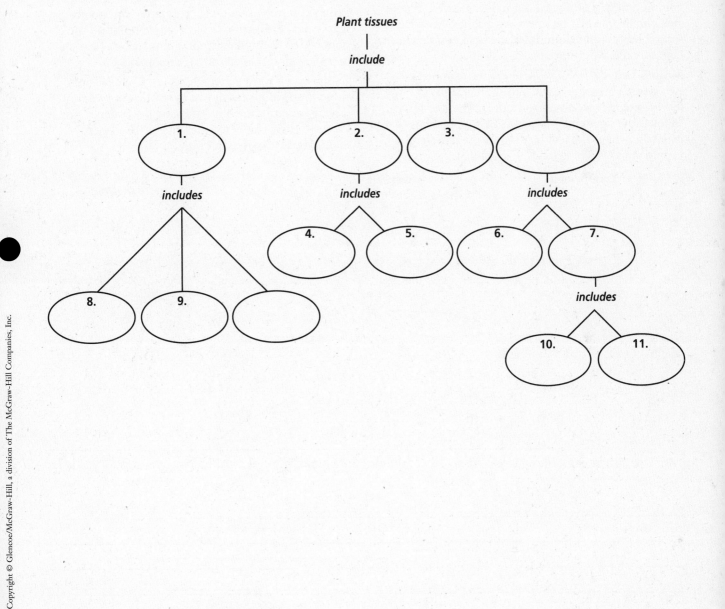

Problem Solving

Use with Chapter 23, Section 23.2

Using a Key to Identify Trees

There are many different keys that can be used for identifying common deciduous trees. Identification may be based on leaves, flowers, fruits, bark, and even twigs and buds. Perhaps the most common means of identification is by leaves. The first choice of a leaf type in a key might be between simple leaves (one main leaf blade on a petiole) and compound leaves (more than one leaflet on a petiole).

Simple Leaves   *Simple leaves* can be grouped into two types: (1) maple leaves and similar kinds of leaves, and (2) oak leaves and similar kinds of leaves. Maple leaves generally have three or more veins that originate where the leaf blade joins the petiole. Each vein in a maple leaf extends to a point at the margin

of the leaf. Oak leaves have one main vein called a midrib coming from the petiole and smaller veins leading to leaf lobes on each side of the vein.

Compound Leaves   *Compound leaves* can also be grouped into two types: (1) palmately compound leaves (leaflets coming from a single point on the petiole), or (2) pinnately compound leaves (leaflets arranged along the length of the petiole).

Suppose you were given five leaves from each of these four groups, as shown in the diagrams below. The leaves are shown in no particular order. Observe their characteristics and write a key to identify and classify each leaf.

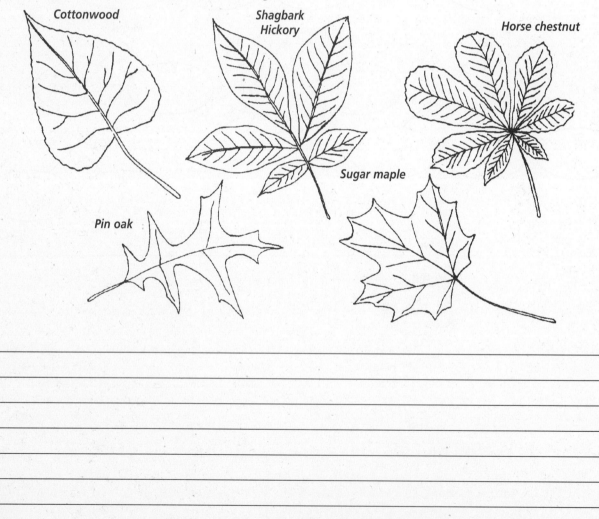

Cottonwood

Shagbark Hickory

Horse chestnut

Sugar maple

Pin oak

_____
_____
_____
_____
_____
_____
_____
_____

Master 55 **Plant Cells and Tissues**

Use with Chapter 23, Section 23.1

Apple cross section

Tree cross section

Leaf cross section

❶ What different types of tissues are found in these plants?

❷ What is the function of these different tissues?

Section Focus

Master
56 **Angiosperm Structures**

Use with Chapter 23, Section 23.2

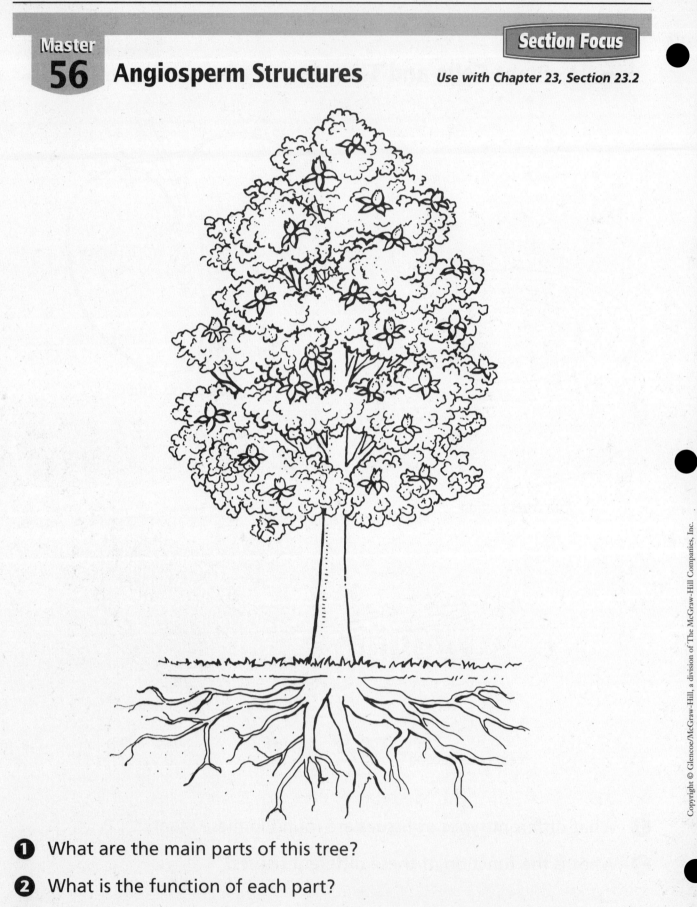

❶ What are the main parts of this tree?

❷ What is the function of each part?

Name _____ Date _____ Class _____

Master
57 **Plant Responses**

❶ To what stimuli is this plant responding?

❷ Can this growth pattern be altered? Explain.

Master 36

Functions of Stomata

Basic Concepts

Use with Chapter 23, Section 23.2

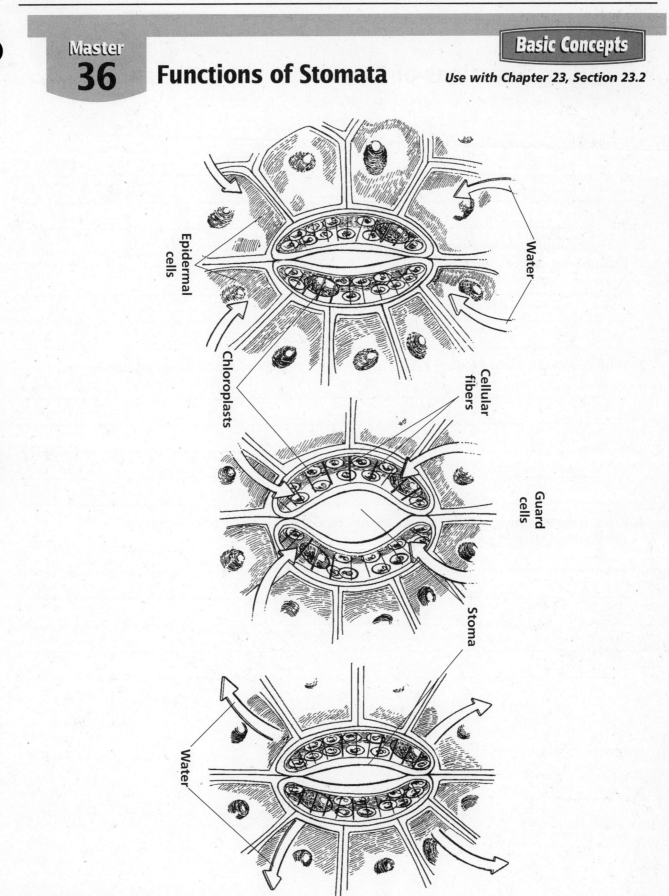

Epidermal cells

Water

Chloroplasts

Cellular fibers

Guard cells

Stoma

Water

1. Under what conditions does the size of a stomatal pore change?

_____

_____

_____

2. Which drawing(s) shows a response to dry environmental conditions?
Explain your answer.

_____

_____

_____

3. Why would it be useful for there to be a large number of chloroplasts in the guard cells?

_____

_____

_____

_____

4. Refer to the transparency to explain what happens to the guard cells when there is an
abundance of water in surrounding cells.

_____

_____

_____

_____

_____

Master
37
Leaf Structure

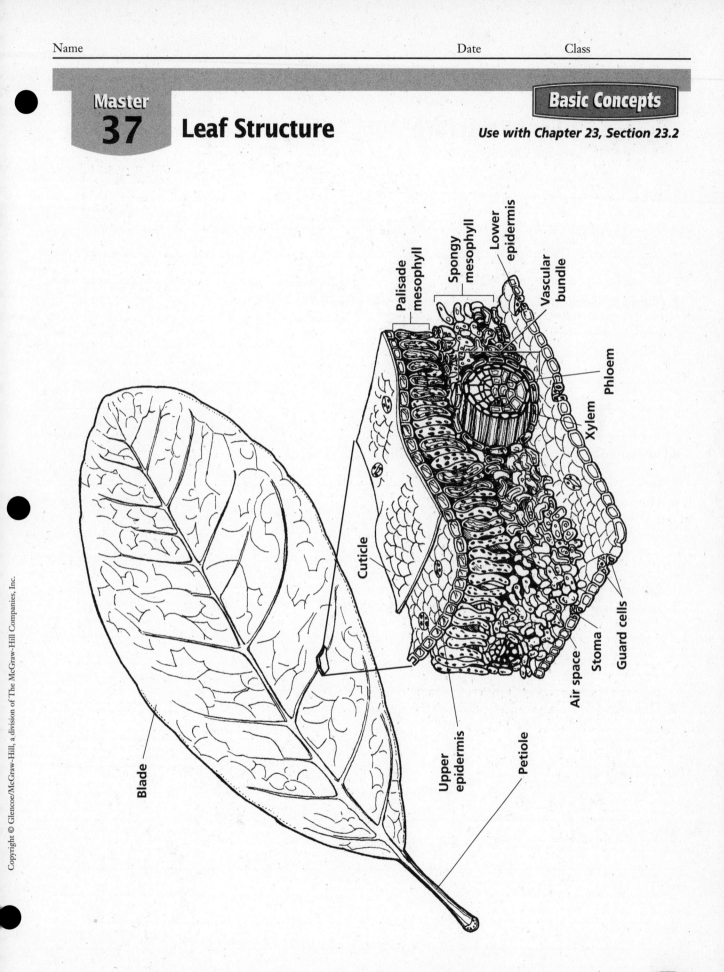

Palisade mesophyll

Spongy mesophyll

Lower epidermis

Vascular bundle

Phloem

Xylem

Cuticle

Air space

Stoma

Guard cells

Upper epidermis

Petiole

Blade

Worksheet 37 Leaf Structure

1. What is the primary function of leaves?

_____

_____

_____

2. Through which structures does transpiration take place?

_____

3. What is the structure and function of a cuticle?

_____

_____

_____

4. In what part of the leaf does most photosynthesis take place?

_____

5. What substances pass through the stomata?

_____

_____

_____

6. In what leaf structures are the xylem and phloem located?

_____

_____

_____

7. Describe the structure and function of the spongy mesophyll.

_____

_____

_____

_____

8. What is a petiole?

_____

_____

_____

Master 32

What Is the Function of Trichomes?

Reteaching Skills

Use with Chapter 23, Section 23.1

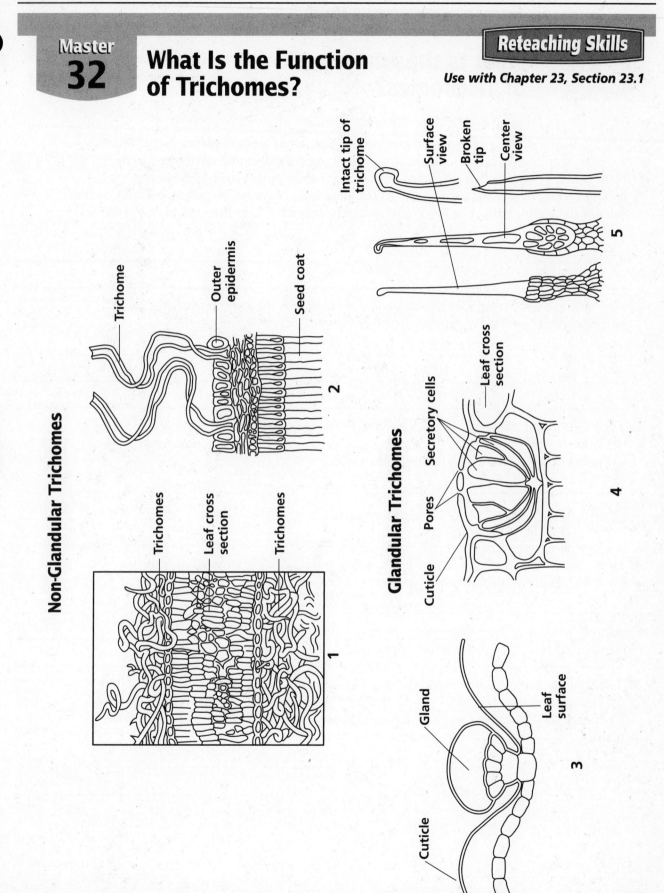

Non-Glandular Trichomes

Trichome

Outer epidermis

Seed coat

2

Trichomes

Leaf cross section

Trichomes

1

Glandular Trichomes

Secretory cells

Leaf cross section

Pores

Cuticle

4

Gland

Leaf surface

Cuticle

3

Intact tip of trichome

Surface view

Broken tip

Center view

5

Worksheet 32

What Is the Function of Trichomes?

1. The transparency shows a variety of trichomes on different kinds of plants. A trichome is a modified epidermal cell. Think about the advantages of each kind of trichome to the plant listed. What adaptive advantage would there be for a plant such as the desert composite *Encelia farinosa*, brittlebush (#1), to have mats of trichomes covering both sides of the leaves. Hint: The hairy mats shade the leaf more than other plants that lack these trichomes.

_____

2. How would the short hairs on the seed coats of *Gossypium*, the cotton plant (#2), be an adaptive advantage if the plant were left to grow wild?

_____

_____

3. The oil-secreting glands of thyme, *Thymus capitatus* (#3), produce the fragrance and taste of the herb. Another oil-secretor, *Mentha*, provides a mint flavor. Hypothesize the adaptive value of the oil secretions to these plants.

_____

_____

_____

4. *Limonium latifolium*, the sea lavender (#4), grows in saline habitats, often near the sea. How do salt-gland trichomes help this plant to survive?

_____

_____

_____

5. The stinging hairs of *Urtica dioica*, the stinging nettle (#5), are glandular trichomes. The tip of the needlelike hairs break off, leaving a syringe that penetrates the skin and injects irritants such as histamine and acetylcholine. How might these trichomes protect this plant?

_____

_____

Master 33

Internal Structure of a Leaf *Use with Chapter 23, Section 23.2*

Photosynthesis

Storage of gases

Regulates flow in veins

Conducts water and dissolved minerals to leaf from roots

Conducts sugars from leaf to plant

Allows gases to flow within leaf

Location of many stomata

Transpiration

Waxy protective coating

Carbon dioxide and oxygen enter leaf

Oxygen and water vapor exit leaf

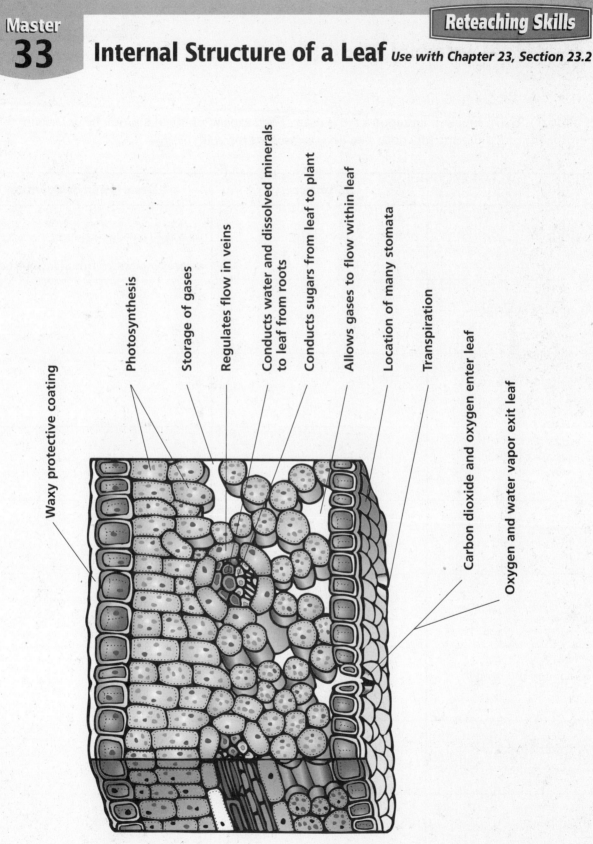

Worksheet 33

Internal Structure of a Leaf Use with Chapter 23, Section 23.2

To fill in this chart, supply a definition for the term. Then expand on the definition by describing the item and/or indicating the item's function. The first one is done for you.

	Definition	Description or Function
cuticle	protective, waxy layer	**a.** waxy coating **b.** prevents water from leaving the leaf
1. upper epidermis		**a.** **b.**
2. palisade mesophyll		**a.** **b.**
3. vascular bundle		**a.** **b.**
4. xylem		**a.** **b.**
5. phloem		**a.** **b.**
6. spongy mesophyll		**a.** **b.**
7. lower epidermis		**a.** **b.**
8. stomata		**a.** **b.**

Master 34

A Plant's Vascular System

Use with Chapter 23, Section 23.2

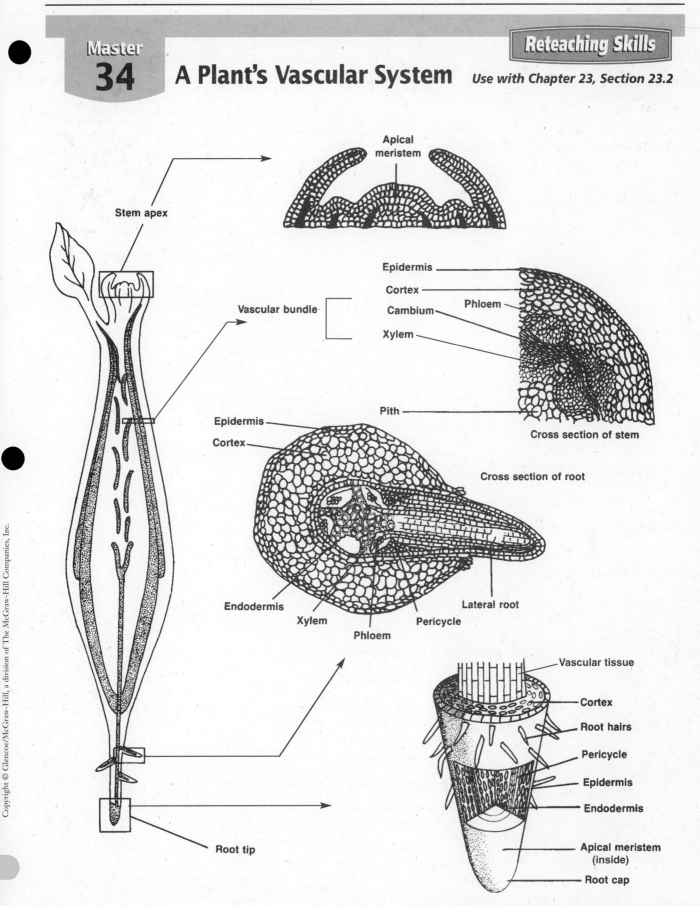

Apical meristem

Stem apex

Vascular bundle

Epidermis
Cortex
Cambium
Phloem
Xylem

Pith

Cross section of stem

Epidermis
Cortex

Cross section of root

Endodermis
Xylem
Phloem
Pericycle
Lateral root

Vascular tissue
Cortex
Root hairs
Pericycle
Epidermis
Endodermis
Apical meristem (inside)
Root cap

Root tip

Worksheet 34 — A Plant's Vascular System

Use with Chapter 23, Section 23.2

1. Explain how the functions of xylem and phloem differ.

_____

_____

_____

_____

2. In what part of a stem are some leaves and flower buds produced?

_____

_____

3. In what part of a stem does secondary vascular tissue grow? What is the result of this growth?

_____

_____

_____

4. Describe the structure and function of a root hair.

_____

_____

_____

_____

5. What tissue gives rise to lateral roots?

_____

_____

6. Which layer of cells forms a waterproof seal around the root?

_____

_____

7. What is the function of cork cambium?

_____

_____

_____

_____

Chapter
23 **Plant Structure and Function**

Reviewing Vocabulary

Match the definition in Column A with the term in Column B.

Column A   **Column B**

_____ **1.** Plant tissue that transports water and dissolved minerals   **a.** apical meristem
from the roots to the rest of the plant

_____ **2.** Tubular cell that is tapered at each end. Its cell wall has   **b.** companion cell
pits through which water and dissolved minerals move
throughout a plant   **c.** epidermis

_____ **3.** Tissue that gives rise to lateral roots   **d.** guard cells

_____ **4.** A responsive movement of a plant that is not
dependent on the direction of the stimulus   **e.** hormone

_____ **5.** Stalk that joins the leaf blade to the stem   **f.** mesophyll

_____ **6.** A portion of the plant that uses or stores sugars   **g.** nastic movement

_____ **7.** Flattened parenchyma cells that cover all parts of
the plant   **h.** cortex

_____ **8.** Tissue composed of living cells that transport sugars   **i.** pericycle
to all parts of the plant

_____ **9.** Growth tissue that remains just behind the root tip   **j.** petiole

_____ **10.** Contains a nucleus and helps control movement   **k.** phloem
through the sieve cell

_____ **11.** A plant's response to an external stimulus that comes   **l.** sink
from a particular direction

_____ **12.** A chemical that is produced in one part of an   **m.** tracheid
organism and transported to another part, where
it causes a physiological change.   **n.** tropism

_____ **13.** Cells that surround and control the opening of   **o.** xylem
a stoma

_____ **14.** Photosynthetic tissue of a leaf

_____ **15.** Tissue in the root that can act as a storage area
for food and water

Chapter 23 **Plant Structure and Function,** *continued*

Chapter Assessment

Understanding Main Ideas (Part A)

In the space at the left, write the letter of the word or phrase that best completes the statement or answers the question.

_____ **1.** To control water loss, the size of a stoma is reduced by the
    a. xylem.   **b.** phloem.   **c.** cambium.   **d.** guard cells.

_____ **2.** Xylem is vascular tissue that
    a. is alive.
    b. transports sugar from the leaves to all parts of the plant.
    c. transports water and dissolved minerals from the roots to all parts of a plant.
    d. transports sperm to the eggs.

_____ **3.** Cells in the apical meristem that cause a root to grow longer are found
    a. just behind the root tip.   **b.** along the sides of the root.
    c. at the top of the root.   **d.** in the center of the root.

_____ **4.** What area is responsible for producing the cells that allow the roots and stems to increase in length?
    a. apical meristem   **b.** vascular meristem   **c.** pericycle   **d.** endodermis

_____ **5.** What is the primary function of plant leaves?
    a. to support the plant   **b.** to produce flowers
    c. to take in water   **d.** photosynthesis

_____ **6.** Where does most photosynthesis take place?
    a. in the cells of the cortex   **b.** in the spongy mesophyll
    c. in the palisade mesophyll   **d.** in the stomata

_____ **7.** The petiole and veins of a leaf contain the
    a. apical meristem.   **b.** epidermis.   **c.** endodermis.   **d.** vascular tissue.

In the space at the left, write <u>true</u> if the statement is true. If the statement is false, change the italicized word or phrase to make it true.

_____ **8.** A *root cap* is a tiny extension of a single epidermal cell that increases the surface area of the root and absorbs water, oxygen, and dissolved minerals.

_____ **9.** The loss of water from the stomata of the leaves is called *perspiration*.

_____ **10.** A *vessel element* is a tubular cell that transports water throughout the plant.

Understanding Main Ideas (Part B)

Answer the following questions.

1. What causes tree rings to form?

   _____

   _____

   _____

   _____

2. How do auxims promote cell elongation?

   _____

   _____

   _____

   _____

   _____

3. Explain why fruit kept in a closed container ripens more quickly than fruit left out in an open bowl.

   _____

   _____

   _____

4. How do guard cells prevent a plant from drying out?

   _____

   _____

   _____

   _____

   _____

5. What are the functions of a root?

   _____

   _____

   _____

Chapter 23 **Plant Structure and Function,** *continued*

Thinking Critically

Answer the following questions.

1. A researcher performed an experiment to determine the function of xylem and phloem. He removed the bark, including the phloem, in a complete ring around a tree. The xylem was left intact. After doing this, the researcher noticed a swelling just above the stripped ring; a sweet fluid leaked from this swollen area. The leaves of the tree remained green for several weeks. Eventually, however, they died; the entire tree died soon after. What could the researcher conclude from this experiment? Explain.

_____

_____

_____

_____

_____

_____

2. The table at the right shows the transpiration rate of some plants measured in liters per day. Why would the transpiration rate of the cactus be so much lower than that of the other plants?

_____

_____

_____

_____

Plant	Liters/Day
Cactus	0.02
Tomato	1.00
Apple	19.00

3. When he was 12 years old, Joe carved his initials into the bark of a tree in the forest behind his house. The tree was 7 m tall and 20 cm in diameter, and the initials were 1.5 m above the ground. When Joe was 22 years old, he went back to see the tree; it had grown to a height of 10 m and was now 27 cm in diameter. How far above the ground were Joe's initials? Explain.

_____

_____

_____

_____

_____

Applying Scientific Methods

Students often perform a simple experiment to verify the fact that water is transported upward from the roots of a plant to its leaves. You may remember that, when you place a celery stalk in colored water, after a few hours, the color reaches the leaves at the top of the celery stalk.

1. Why might you infer that water also reaches the leaves?

_____

_____

_____

This experiment may lead you to formulate a question about water transport in plants. What causes the water to rise from the roots to the leaves against the force of gravity? The answer is that some other force, greater than the gravitational pull on the water, must pull the water upward. In the tallest sequoias, for example, water must rise about 107 m from roots to top leaves. Quite a pull is needed to get the water up to that height.

The answer lies in transpiration. Transpiration occurs as water evaporates from the stomata in the leaves. Scientists think that it is transpiration that provides the force that pulls the water upward against the force of gravity. As water at the stomata evaporates, the water in the leaf just below the stomata is drawn up to replace the vaporized water. Through this process, water slowly and continuously rises to the leaves.

2. Formulate a hypothesis about how temperature could affect the flow of water upward.

_____

_____

_____

3. Plan an experiment to prove your hypothesis.

_____

_____

_____

_____

4. What will be your control in this experiment?

_____

_____

_____

5. What is the variable in this experiment?

_____

_____

Chapter
23 **Plant Structure and Function,** *continued*

Applying Scientific Methods   *continued*

6. Transpiration occurs only during the day. Hypothesize why this might be.

_____

_____

_____

7. How would you verify your hypothesis?

_____

_____

_____

8. What will be your control in this experiment?

_____

_____

_____

9. What is the variable in this experiment?

_____

_____

Chapter Assessment

Chapter 23 Assessment
Student Recording Sheet

Use with pages 630–631 of the Student Edition

Vocabulary Review

Write the word you chose and explain why it does not belong.

1. _____   4. _____

2. _____   5. _____

3. _____

Understanding Key Concepts

Select the best answer from the choices given and fill in the corresponding oval.

6. Ⓐ Ⓑ Ⓒ Ⓓ   10. Ⓐ Ⓑ Ⓒ Ⓓ

7. Ⓐ Ⓑ Ⓒ Ⓓ   11. Ⓐ Ⓑ Ⓒ Ⓓ

8. Ⓐ Ⓑ Ⓒ Ⓓ   12. Ⓐ Ⓑ Ⓒ Ⓓ

9. Ⓐ Ⓑ Ⓒ Ⓓ

Constructed Response

Record your answers for Questions 13 and 14 on a separate sheet of paper.

Thinking Critically

Record your answer for Question 15 on a separate sheet of paper.

16. **REAL WORLD BIOCHALLENGE** Follow your teacher's instructions for presenting your BioChallenge answer.

Standardized Test Practice

Part 1 Multiple Choice

Select the best answer from the choices given and fill in the corresponding oval.

17. Ⓐ Ⓑ Ⓒ Ⓓ

18. Ⓐ Ⓑ Ⓒ Ⓓ

19. Ⓐ Ⓑ Ⓒ Ⓓ

20. Ⓐ Ⓑ Ⓒ Ⓓ

Part 2
Constructed Response/Grid In

Record your answers for Questions 21 and 22 on a separate sheet of paper.

Contents

Chapter 24 Reproduction in Plants

BioDigest 7 Plants

Chapter 24

MiniLab 24.1   Growing Plants Asexually

Plants are capable of reproducing asexually. Reproductive cells such as egg or sperm are not needed in asexual reproduction. Plants are able to use structures such as roots, stems, and even leaves to produce new offspring.

Procedure

1 Prepare three different plant parts for study using diagrams A, B, and C on page 634 of your text as a guide.

2 Design a data table that will provide enough room for diagrams of your observations. The number of days since the start of the experiment should be included.

3 Make your initial diagrams of the plant parts today and label these diagrams as "Day 1."

4 Observations should be made every three days. Replace any lost water as needed.

5 Observe any changes that occur to your plants over the next two weeks.

Analysis

1. What experimental evidence do you have that:

   a. plants use a variety of structures for asexual reproduction?

   _____

   _____

   b. asexual reproduction is a rapid process?

   _____

   c. asexual reproduction requires only one parent?

   _____

2. Describe several advantages of asexual reproduction in plants.

   _____

   _____

   _____

   _____

MiniLab 24.2 **Looking at Germinating Seeds**   *Observing*

Seeds are made up of a plant embryo, a seed coat, and in some plants, a food-storage tissue. Monocot and dicot seeds differ in their internal structures.

Procedure 🥽 ✋ ☣️

1 Obtain from your teacher a soaked, ungerminated corn kernel (monocot), a bean seed (dicot), and corn and bean seeds that have begun to germinate.

2 Remove the seed coats from each of the ungerminated seeds, and examine the structures inside. Use low-power magnification. Locate and identify each structure of the embryo and any other structures you observe.

3 Examine the germinating seeds. Locate and identify the structures you observed in the dormant seeds.

Analysis

1. Diagram the dormant embryos in the soaked seeds, and label their structures. Diagram the germinating seeds, and label their structures.

2. List at least three major differences you observed in the internal structures of the corn and bean seeds.

_____

_____

_____

INVESTIGATE BioLab

Examining the Organs of a Flower

Chapter **24**

PREPARATION

Problem

What do the organs of a flower look like? How are they arranged?

Objectives

In this BioLab, you will:
- **Observe** the organs of a flower.
- **Identify** the functions of flower organs.

Materials

flower—any complete dicot flower that is available locally, such as phlox, carnation, or tobacco flower
hand lens (or stereomicroscope)
colored pencils (red, green, blue)
2 microscope slides
water

dropper
2 coverslips
microscope
single-edged razor blade
forceps (or tweezers)

Safety Precautions

Handle the razor blade with extreme caution. Always cut away from you. Use caution when handling a microscope, coverslips, and slides. Wash your hands with soap and water after handling plant material.

Skill Handbook

Use the **Skill Handbook** if you need additional help with this lab.

PROCEDURE

1. Examine your flower. Locate the sepals and petals. Note their numbers, size, color, and arrangement on the flower stem. Remove the sepals and petals from your flower by gently pulling them off the stem.

2. Locate the stamens, each of which consists of a thin filament with a pollen-filled anther on the tip. Note and record the number of stamens.

3. Locate the pistil. The stigma at the top of the pistil is often sticky. The style is a long, narrow structure that leads from the stigma to the ovary.

4. Place an anther from one of the stamens onto a microscope slide and add a drop of water. Cut the anther into several pieces with the razor blade. **CAUTION:** *Always take care when using a razor blade.*

5. Examine the anther under low and high power of your microscope. The small, dotlike structures are pollen grains.

6. Slice the pistil in half lengthwise with the razor blade. Mount one half, cut side facing

up, on a microscope slide.

7. Identify and examine the ovary with a hand lens or dissecting microscope. The many small, dotlike structures that fill the two ovary halves are ovules. Each ovule contains an egg cell that is not visible under low power. A tiny stalk connects each ovule to the ovary wall.

8. Make a diagram of the flower, labeling all its parts. Color the female reproductive parts red. Color the male reproductive parts green. Color the remaining parts blue.

9. **Cleanup and Disposal** Clean all equipment as instructed by your teacher, and return everything to its proper place. Properly dispose of coverslips and flower organs. Wash your hands thoroughly.

INVESTIGATE
BioLab

Examining the Structure of a Flower, *continued*

Chapter **24**

ANALYZE AND CONCLUDE

1. Observing How many stamens are present in your flower? How many pistils, ovaries, sepals, and petals?

_____

_____

_____

2. Comparing and Contrasting Make a reasonable estimate of the number of pollen grains in the anther and the number of ovules in an ovary of your flower. Calculate the class average of the estimated number of pollen grains and estimated number of ovules.

_____

_____

3. Interpreting Data Which produces more? Pollen grains by one anther? Ovules produced by one ovary? Give a possible explanation for your answer.

_____

_____

_____

_____

_____

Reproduction in Plants

Section 24.1 Life Cycles of Mosses, Ferns, and Conifers

In your textbook, read about alternation of generations and the life cycles of mosses and ferns.

Use each of the terms below just once to complete the following statements.

diploid	meiosis	sporophyte
dominant	mitosis	vegetative reproduction
egg	protonema	
gametophyte	sperm	

1. The two phases of the plant life are the _____ stage and

    the _____ stage.

2. The cells of the sporophyte are all _____ .

3. The female gamete is the _____ , and the male gamete is the _____ .

4. Some plants reproduce asexually by a process called _____ , in which a new

    plant is produced from an existing vegetative structure.

5. Mosses belong to one of the few plant divisions in which the gametophyte plant is the

    _____ generation.

6. A small, green filament of moss cells that develops into either a male or female moss gametophyte is

    known as a(n) _____ .

7. The moss diploid zygote divides by _____ to form a new sporophyte in the

    form of a stalk and capsule.

8. Spores are produced by _____ in the capsule of the moss sporophyte.

**Number each description to order the stages from spore release of the life cycle
of a fern, from 1 to 7.**

_____ **9.** A spore germinates and grows into a heart-shaped gametophyte called a prothallus.

_____ **10.** After fertilization, the diploid zygote grows into a sporophyte.

_____ **11.** As the sporophyte grows, roots and fronds grow out from the rhizome.

_____ **12.** Sperm swim through a film of water on the prothallus to reach and fertilize an egg in
the archegonium.

_____ **13.** In each sporangium, spores are produced by meiosis, and the cycle begins again as the
spores are dispersed by the wind.

_____ **14.** Sori, or clusters of sporangia, grow on the pinnae.

_____ **15.** A sporangium bursts, releasing haploid spores.

Section 24.1 Life Cycles of Mosses, Ferns, and Conifers

In your textbook, read about the life cycle of conifers.

Answer the following questions.

1. What is the dominant stage in conifers?

   _____

2. What does the adult conifer produce on its branches?

   _____

   _____

3. What is a megaspore?

   _____

   _____

4. What are microspores and how are they produced?

   _____

   _____

5. What do the microspores develop into?

   _____

6. What is a micropyle?

   _____

7. How does fertilization take place?

   _____

   _____

   _____

   _____

8. After fertilization, a zygote develops inside the ovule into an embryo with several cotyledons. What happens to the ovule?

   _____

   _____

9. What happens to the seeds when the female cone opens and falls to the ground?

   _____

   _____

10. What will the seedling become?

   _____

Chapter
24 **Reproduction in Plants,** *continued*

Section 24.2 Flowers and Flowering

In your textbook, read about the structure of a flower.

Determine if the statement is true. If it is not, rewrite the italicized part to make it true.

1. In flowering plants, sexual reproduction takes place in the *seed*, which has several parts.

_____

2. The structure of a flower includes four kinds of organs: *sepals, petals, stamens, and ovaries.*

_____

3. *Petals* are usually colorful, leaflike structures that encircle the flower stem.

_____

4. The male reproductive structure located inside the petals of a flower is a *stamen*. Sperm-containing pollen is produced in the *anther* at the tip of the stamen.

_____

5. The female reproductive structure at the center of a flower is the *ovary*. Eggs are formed in the *pistil*, which is located in the bottom portion of the *ovary*.

_____

Label the parts of the flower. Use these choices:

sepal	petal	stigma	ovule
anther	ovary	filament	

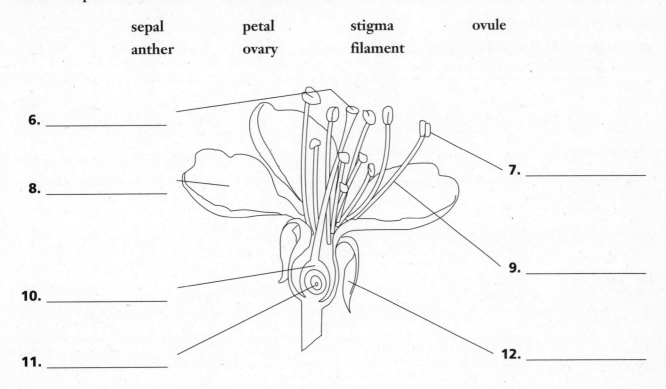

6. _____

8. _____

10. _____

11. _____

7. _____

9. _____

12. _____

Chapter 24 Reproduction in Plants, *continued*

Section 24.3 The Life Cycle of a Flowering Plant

In your textbook, read about the life cycle of a flowering plant.

For each item in Column A, write the letter of the matching item from Column B.

Column A		Column B
_____	**1.** Two nuclei in one cell at the center of the embryo sac	**a.** dormancy
_____	**2.** A process in which one sperm fertilizes the egg and the other sperm joins with the central cell	**b.** double fertilization
_____	**3.** Food-storing tissue that develops from the triploid central cell and supports the development of the embryo	**c.** endosperm
_____	**4.** A period of inactivity in which seeds of some plant species remain until conditions are favorable for growth and development	**d.** germination
_____	**5.** The beginning of the development of the embryo into a new plant	**e.** hypocotyl
_____	**6.** This embryonic root is the first part of the embryo to appear from the seed	**f.** polar nuclei
_____	**7.** The portion of the stem near the seed	**g.** radicle

Answer the following questions.

8. How do anthophytes attract animal pollinators?

_____

_____

9. How do seeds form after fertilization takes place?

_____

_____

_____

10. Name three ways seeds are dispersed.

_____

_____

_____

_____

Capítulo 24 Reproducción de las plantas

Sección 24.1 *Ciclo de vida de musgos, helechos y coníferas*

En tu libro de texto, lee sobre la alternancia de generaciones y los ciclos de vida de musgos y helechos.

Completa el párrafo usando cada término una sola vez.

diploide   meiosis   esporofita
dominante   mitosis   reproducción vegetativa
huevo   protonema
gametofita   espermatozoide

1. Las dos fases en la vida de una planta son la generación _____ y la generación _____ .

2. Todas las células del esporofito son _____ .

3. El gameto femenino es el _____ mientras que el masculino es el _____ .

4. Algunas plantas se reproducen asexualmente mediante un proceso llamado _____ , en el que una planta se reproduce a partir de una estructura vegetativa.

5. Los musgos pertenecen a una de las pocas divisiones de plantas en que el gametofito es la generación _____ .

6. El filamento verde y pequeño de células de un musgo que se convierte en un gametofito femenino o masculino se conoce como _____ .

7. El cigoto diploide del musgo se divide mediante _____ para formar un nuevo esporofito con forma de tallo y cápsula.

8. La _____ produce esporas en la cápsula del esporofito del musgo.

Enumera del 1 al 7 los siguientes enunciados, de acuerdo con el orden en que ocurren a partir de la liberación de las esporas por parte del helecho.

_____ 9. La espora germina, crece y se convierte en el gametofito de forma acorazonada llamado prótalo.

_____ 10. Después de la fecundación, el cigoto diploide crece y se convierte en el esporofito.

_____ 11. Al crecer el esporofito, al rizoma le crecen raíces y frondas.

_____ 12. El espermatozoide nada a través de una película de agua en el prótalo, para llegar hasta el ovocito situado en el arquegonio y fecundarlo.

_____ 13. Se producen esporas por meiosis en los esporangios y se inicia nuevamente el ciclo, al ser dispersadas por el viento las esporas.

_____ 14. Crecen soros, o conjuntos de esporangios, en las pinas.

_____ 15. El esporangio se abre, liberando las esporas haploides.

Reproducción de las plantas,
continuación

Sección 24.1 Ciclo de vida de musgos, helechos y coníferas

En tu libro de texto, lee sobre el ciclo de vida de las coníferas.

Contesta las siguientes preguntas.

1. ¿Cuál es la generación dominante en las coníferas?

_____

2. ¿Qué produce en sus ramas una conífera adulta?

_____

_____

3. ¿Qué es una megáspora?

_____

_____

4. ¿Qué son las micrósporas y cómo se producen?

_____

_____

5. ¿En qué se convierten las micrósporas?

_____

6. ¿Qué es el micrópilo?

_____

7. ¿Cómo ocurre la fecundación?

_____

_____

_____

_____

8. Después de la fecundación, el cigoto rodeado por el integumento del óvulo se desarrolla en un embrión con varios cotiledones. ¿Qué le ocurre al óvulo?

_____

_____

9. ¿Qué les ocurre a las semillas cuando el cono femenino se abre y cae al suelo?

_____

_____

10. ¿En qué se convertirá la plántula?

_____

_____

Capítulo 24 **Reproducción de las plantas,** continuación

En tu libro de texto, lee sobre la estructura de la flor.

Si el enunciado es verdadero, escribe *verdadero*; de lo contrario, modifica la sección en itálicas para hacer verdadero el enunciado.

1. En las plantas con flores la reproducción sexual ocurre en las *semillas*, que son estructuras formadas de varias partes.

   _____

2. La estructura de una flor incluye cuatro tipos de órganos: *sépalos, pétalos, estambres y ovarios.*

   _____

3. En general, los *pétalos* son estructuras parecidas a hojas de color atractivo que rodean el tallo de la flor.

   _____

4. La estructura reproductora masculina localizada en el interior de los pétalos de una flor es el *estambre*. El polen con los espermatozoides se produce dentro de las *anteras*, que son estructuras localizadas en la punta de los estambres.

   _____

5. La estructura reproductora femenina localizada en el centro de la flor es el *ovario*. Los huevos se forman en el *pistilo*, el cual es la estructura localizada en la base del *ovario*.

   _____

Identifica las partes de la flor. Usa las siguientes opciones:

sépalo	pétalo	estigma	huevo
antera	ovario	filamento	

6. _____

7. _____

8. _____

9. _____

10. _____

11. _____

12. _____

Capítulo 24 **Reproducción de las plantas,**
continuación

Sección 24.3 El ciclo de vida de las plantas con flores

En tu libro de texto, lee sobre el ciclo de vida de las plantas con flores.

Anota la letra de la columna B que corresponda a cada enunciado de la columna A.

Columna A	Columna B
1. Dos núcleos en una de las células en el centro del saco embrionario.	**a.** latencia
2. Proceso durante el cual un espermatozoide fecunda el huevo y otro se fusiona con la célula central.	**b.** doble fecundación
3. Tejido de almacenamiento que se desarrolla a partir de la célula central triploide y que proporciona alimento al embrión en desarrollo.	**c.** endospermo
4. Período de inactividad en que permanecen algunas especies de plantas hasta que encuentran condiciones favorables para el crecimiento y desarrollo.	**d.** germinación
	e. hipocótilo
5. Inicio de la transformación del embrión en una nueva planta.	**f.** núcleos polares
6. Esta raíz embrionaria es la primera parte del embrión que aparece en la semilla.	**g.** radícula
7. Porción del tallo cercana a la semilla.	

Contesta las siguientes preguntas.

8. ¿Cómo atraen las antofitas a los animales polinizadores?

_____

_____

9. ¿Cómo se forma la semilla después de que ocurre la fecundación?

_____

_____

_____

10. Nombra tres mecanismos de dispersión de las semillas.

_____

_____

_____

Chapter
24 Reproduction in Plants

Use with Chapter 24, Section 24.1

Life Cycle of a Fern

Complete the concept map for the life cycle of a fern. Use these words or phrases once: *gametophyte (prothallus), sperm, haploid spores, fronds, antheridia, diploid zygote, eggs, sporangia, archegonia, sori, sporophyte, fertilized egg, rhizome.*

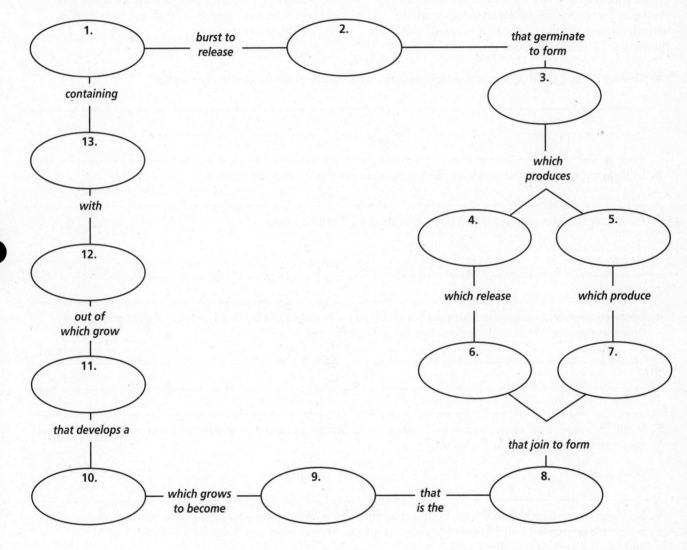

Chapter 24 Reproduction in Plants

Reproduction in Flowering Plants

In flowering plants, seeds develop in a protective structure and are surrounded by a fruit. This gives them an advantage over the less protected seeds of gymnosperms. How did such a helpful adaptation evolve in flowering plants? Researchers working with the desert shrub called "Mormon tea" may have the answer. The Mormon tea shrub has seeds, but the seeds have no endosperm and no fruit is formed. However, observation of the eggs of this plant under a microscope revealed that each ovule had an extra fertilized egg that later died off. Of what use was this extra fertilized egg? To find out, answer the following questions.

1. During double fertilization in flowering plants, what happens to the two sperm nuclei?

_____

_____

2. In flowering plants, what provides the food source for the developing embryo?

_____

3. How may the Mormon tea shrub have used its extra fertilized egg?

_____

_____

4. Some biologists consider the Mormon tea shrub to be an evolutionary link between nonflowering and flowering plants. What evidence do they use to support this view?

_____

_____

5. Some biologists now characterize the endosperm of flowering plants as a "deviant plant embryo." On what evidence might such a view be based?

_____

_____

6. Biologists have hypothesized that, before the evolution of endosperm, plant embryos fed on embryo sacs, which are composed only of maternal cells. As a food source, what evolutionary advantage would endosperm have over embryo sacs?

_____

_____

_____

_____

Master
58 **Fern Life Cycle**

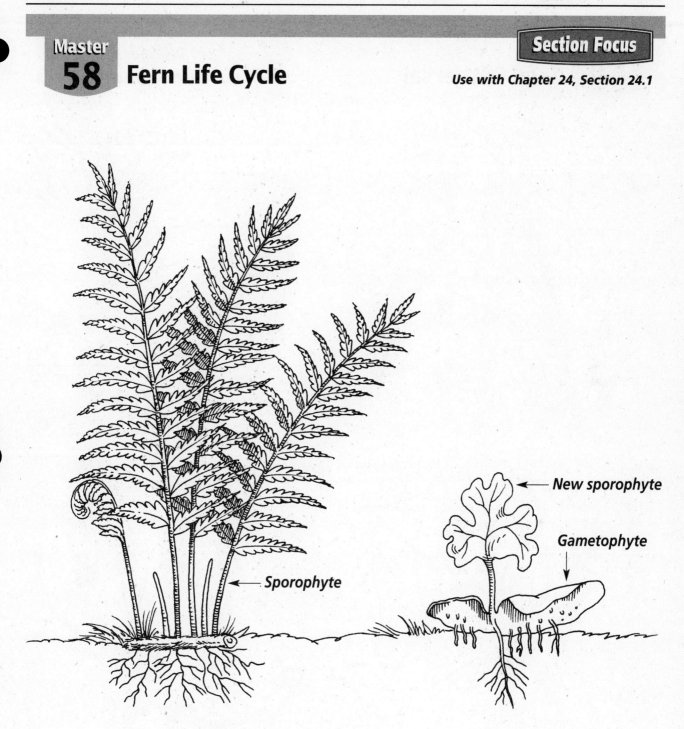

Sporophyte

New sporophyte

Gametophyte

❶ Which generation is dominant in the life cycle of this fern?

❷ How does this compare with the life cycle of mosses?

Master
59 **Seed Dispersal**

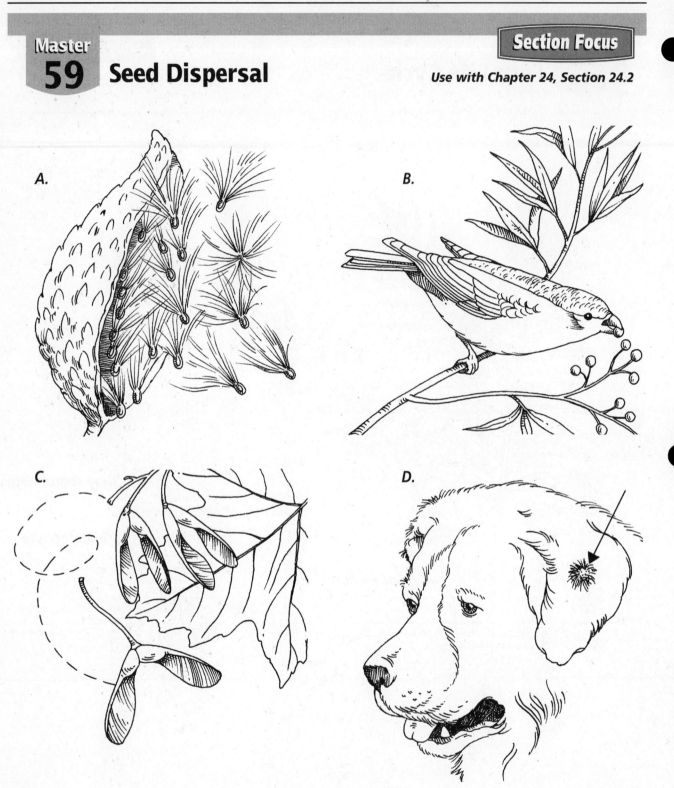

A.

B.

C.

D.

❶ How does the structure of each seed make it suitable for its method of dispersal?

❷ Why is seed dispersal important?

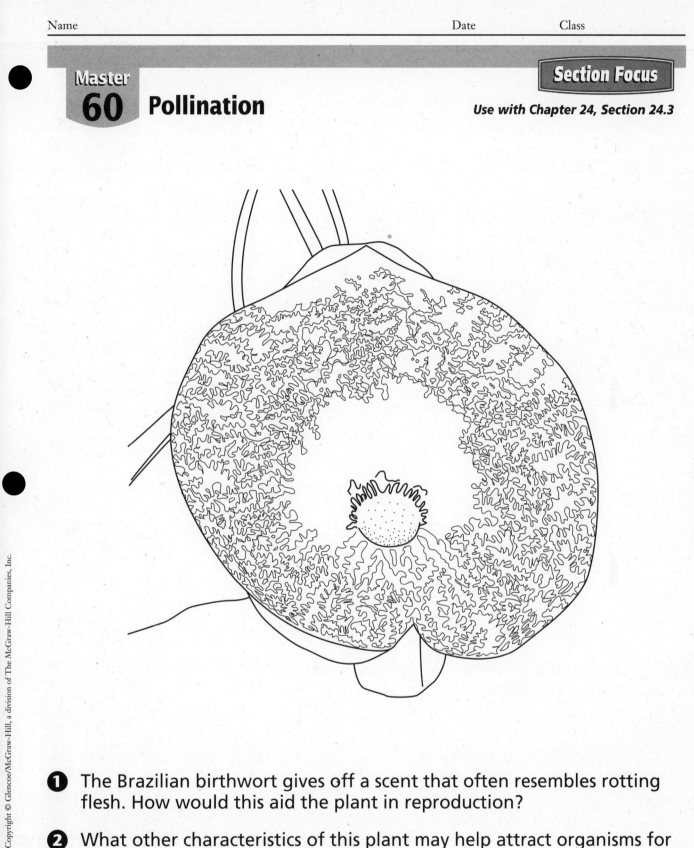

1 The Brazilian birthwort gives off a scent that often resembles rotting flesh. How would this aid the plant in reproduction?

2 What other characteristics of this plant may help attract organisms for the purpose of aiding in reproduction?

Master
38   **Life Cycle of a Moss**

Basic Concepts

Use with Chapter 24, Section 24.1

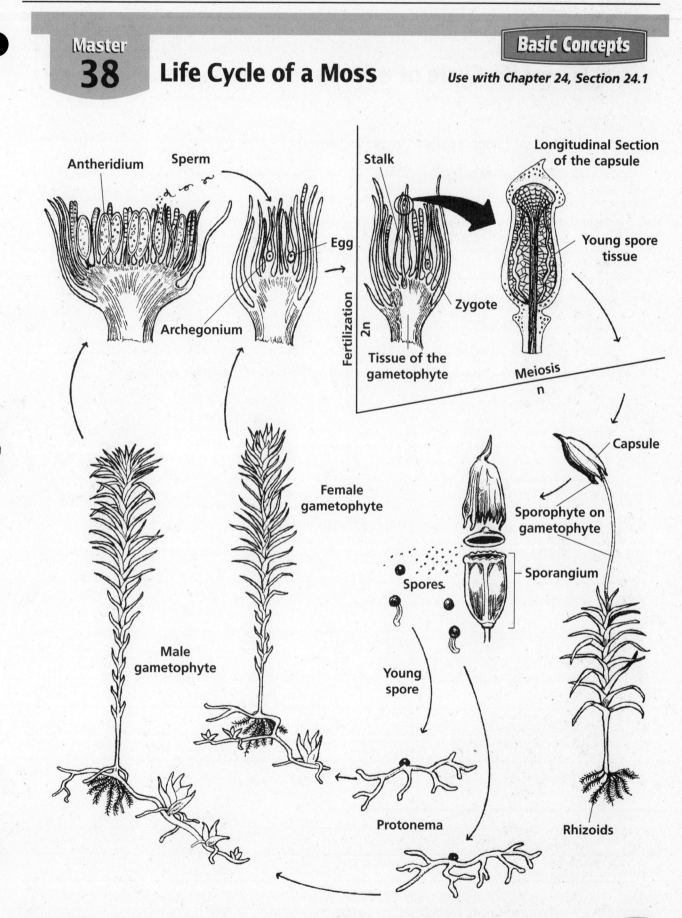

Antheridium   Sperm

Archegonium

Egg

Stalk

Longitudinal Section of the capsule

Young spore tissue

Fertilization
2n

Zygote

Tissue of the gametophyte

Meiosis
n

Capsule

Female gametophyte

Sporophyte on gametophyte

Sporangium

Male gametophyte

Spores

Young spore

Protonema

Rhizoids

Worksheet 38 — Life Cycle of a Moss

Basic Concepts

Use with Chapter 24, Section 24.1

1. Name the two haploid cells produced by gametophytes.

_____

_____

2. How do the cells of a gametophyte differ from those of a sporophyte?

_____

_____

3. Which stage is dominant in the moss life cycle?

_____

_____

4. What structure directly precedes the development of both a male and a female gametophyte?

_____

_____

5. In which structure of a male gametophyte are sperm produced?

_____

_____

6. In which structure of a female gametophyte are eggs produced?

_____

_____

7. What is the product of fertilization in a moss?

_____

_____

8. Explain how a moss can produce offspring at a considerable distance from the parent plant.

_____

_____

_____

9. What abiotic factor is required for fertilization to take place among mosses? Explain your answer.

_____

_____

_____

Master 39 Life Cycle of a Fern

Basic Concepts

Use with Chapter 24, Section 24.1

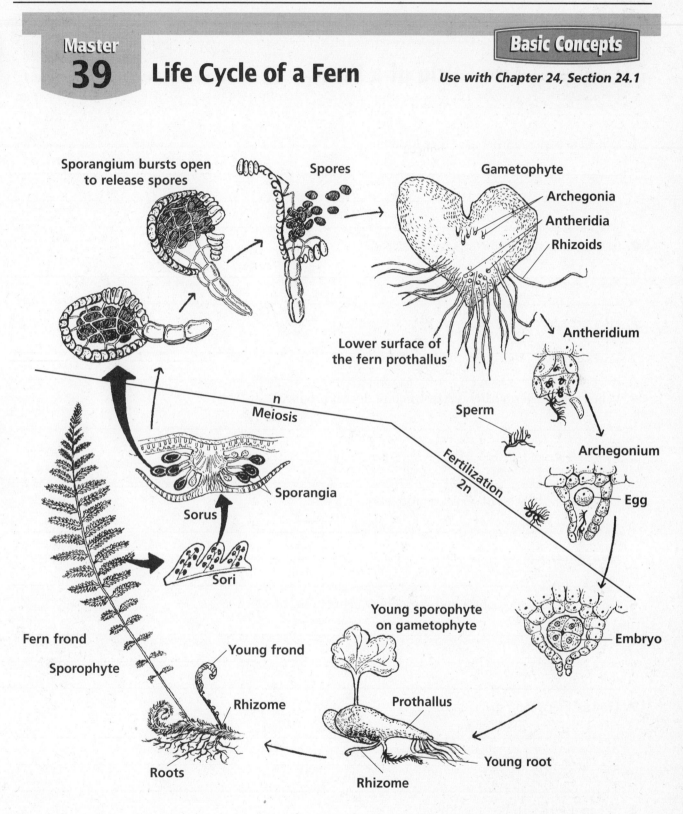

Sporangium bursts open to release spores

Spores

Gametophyte

Archegonia

Antheridia

Rhizoids

Lower surface of the fern prothallus

Antheridium

Sperm

Archegonium

n
Meiosis

Fertilization
2n

Sporangia

Sorus

Egg

Sori

Fern frond

Sporophyte

Embryo

Young sporophyte on gametophyte

Young frond

Prothallus

Rhizome

Young root

Roots

Rhizome

1. What are sori and where are they located?

_____

_____

2. In what structure is the fern egg produced?

_____

_____

3. How are spores dispersed?

_____

_____

4. When a spore germinates, what structure does it produce?

_____

_____

_____

5. Describe the process of sexual reproduction in a fern.

_____

_____

_____

6. Compare the gametophyte and sporophyte generations of a fern.

_____

_____

_____

7. How is a fern stem specialized?

_____

_____

_____

8. When does a fern become diploid?

_____

_____

Master 40 — Life Cycle of a Conifer

Basic Concepts

Use with Chapter 24, Section 24.1

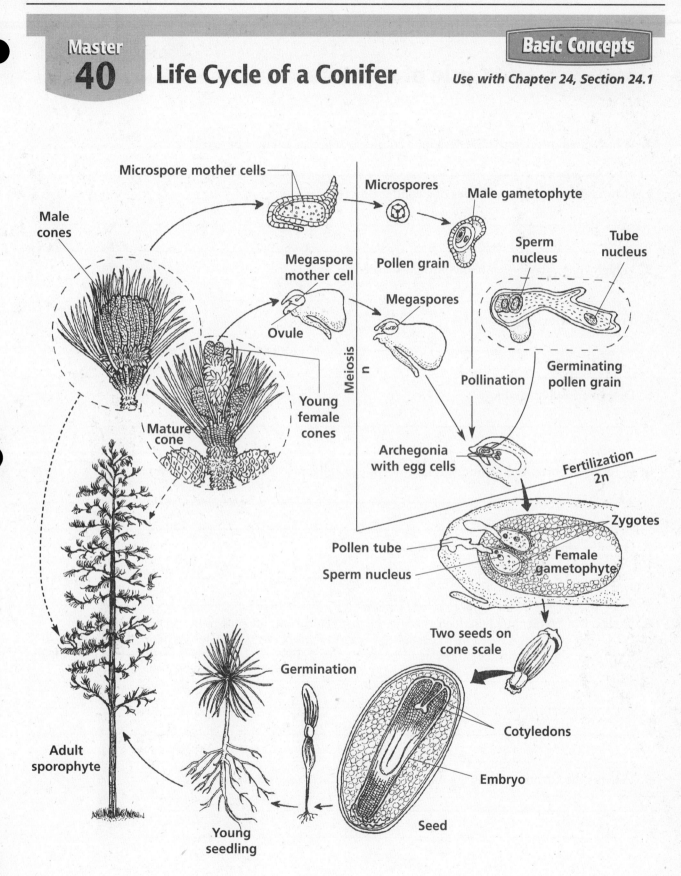

Microspore mother cells

Microspores

Male gametophyte

Male cones

Megaspore mother cell

Pollen grain

Sperm nucleus

Tube nucleus

Megaspores

Ovule

Meiosis
n

Young female cones

Mature cone

Pollination

Germinating pollen grain

Archegonia with egg cells

Fertilization
2n

Zygotes

Pollen tube

Female gametophyte

Sperm nucleus

Two seeds on cone scale

Adult sporophyte

Germination

Cotyledons

Embryo

Young seedling

Seed

Worksheet
40   Life Cycle of a Conifer

Basic Concepts

Use with Chapter 24, Section 24.1

1. Which generation in the life cycle of a conifer is represented by a pine tree?

_____

2. How do the two types of cones of a conifer differ?

_____

_____

3. Which kind of cone eventually produces a seed?

_____

4. Where does meiosis occur?

_____

_____

5. Describe a pollen grain.

_____

_____

6. In terms of chromosome number, how do an egg cell and a sperm cell differ from a seed?

_____

_____

7. Describe what is meant by germination.

_____

_____

8. Explain why conifers are described as being the first plants "fully adapted to life on dry land."

_____

_____

_____

_____

9. What is the adaptive advantage of a plant that produces seeds with "wings"?

_____

_____

Master
41 **Flower Structures**

Basic Concepts

Use with Chapter 24, Section 24.2

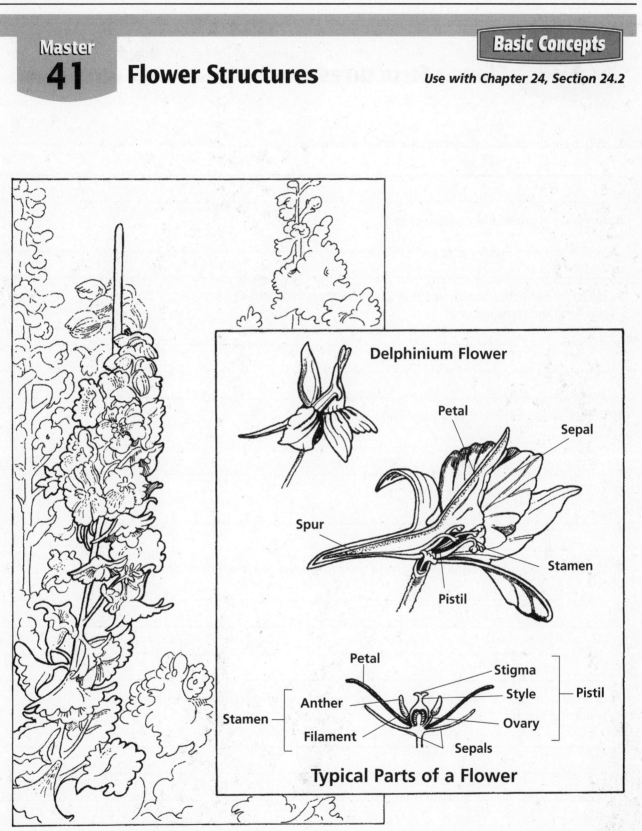

Delphinium Flower

Petal

Sepal

Spur

Stamen

Pistil

Petal

Stigma

Style

Pistil

Anther

Stamen

Ovary

Filament

Sepals

Typical Parts of a Flower

Basic Concepts

Use with Chapter 24, Section 24.2

1. What are the male and female structures of a flower?

_____

_____

2. In which organ would you find eggs?

_____

_____

3. Differentiate between a complete and an incomplete flower. Which kind of flower is shown in the transparency?

_____

_____

_____

4. Which structures make up a pistil and a stamen?

_____

_____

5. What is the function of the sepals?

_____

_____

6. Discuss flower adaptations that increase the probability of cross-pollination.

_____

_____

_____

_____

7. In what general way does pollination differ between nonflowering seed plants and flowering plants?

_____

_____

_____

Master 42

Life Cycle of a Flowering Plant

Pollen sac with microspore mother cells

Anther

Ovary

Microspores in fours

Pollen grain

Meiosis

Ovule with megaspore mother cell

Sperm

Tube nucleus

Male gametophyte

Four megaspores

Egg

GAMETOPHYTE GENERATION
n

Pollen tube

Female gametophyte

SPOROPHYTE GENERATION
2n

Fertilization

Double fertilization

Pollen tube

Zygote

Endosperm nucleus

Adult sporophyte plant

Young seedling

Germinating seed

Seed

Fruit with seeds

**Life Cycle of a
Flowering Plant**

Use with Chapter 24, Section 24.2

1. What happens to a megaspore mother cell and the microspore mother cells as an immediate result of meiosis?

_____

_____

_____

2. Describe the female gametophyte.

_____

_____

3. What is a micropyle?

_____

4. Describe the male gametophyte.

_____

5. What is double fertilization?

_____

_____

_____

6. What is the function of the endosperm?

_____

7. How does a seed develop?

_____

_____

_____

8. What does a fruit consist of?

_____

9. Explain the process of germination by which a seed begins its development into a young seedling.

_____

10. Which generation in the life cycle shown in the transparency is represented by the adult plant?

_____

_____

Master
43

Germination of a Bean Seed

Basic Concepts

Use with Chapter 24, Section 24.3

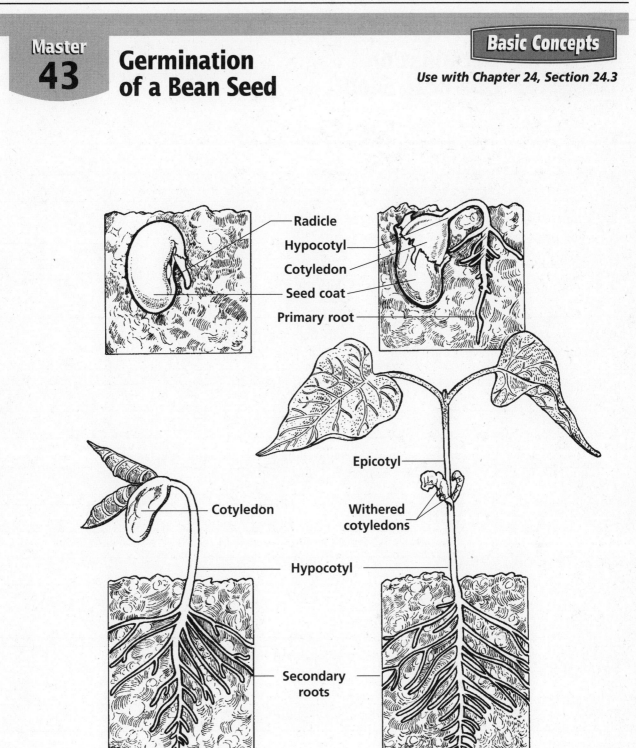

Radicle

Hypocotyl

Cotyledon

Seed coat

Primary root

Epicotyl

Cotyledon

Withered cotyledons

Hypocotyl

Secondary roots

Worksheet 43 — Germination of a Bean Seed

1. What is the first part of the embryo to emerge from the seed?

_____

_____

2. Compare the top two illustrations in the transparency. What is the first part of the young plant to emerge above the soil surface?

_____

3. Before photosynthesis begins, from where does the plant obtain food?

_____

4. What is the function of the period of inactivity before germination? What is the function of the seed coat during this period?

_____

_____

5. List some general requirements for seed germination. What are some special requirements that seeds may have?

_____

_____

_____

_____

_____

6. The transparency reveals the directions in which stems and roots grow. What is the stimulus for these responses? What terms describe the responses?

_____

_____

_____

7. If the stem of the plant in the drawing at the lower right bent to the left over time, what might you infer?

_____

_____

_____

Master 35

Alternation of Generations *Use with Chapter 24, Section 24.1*

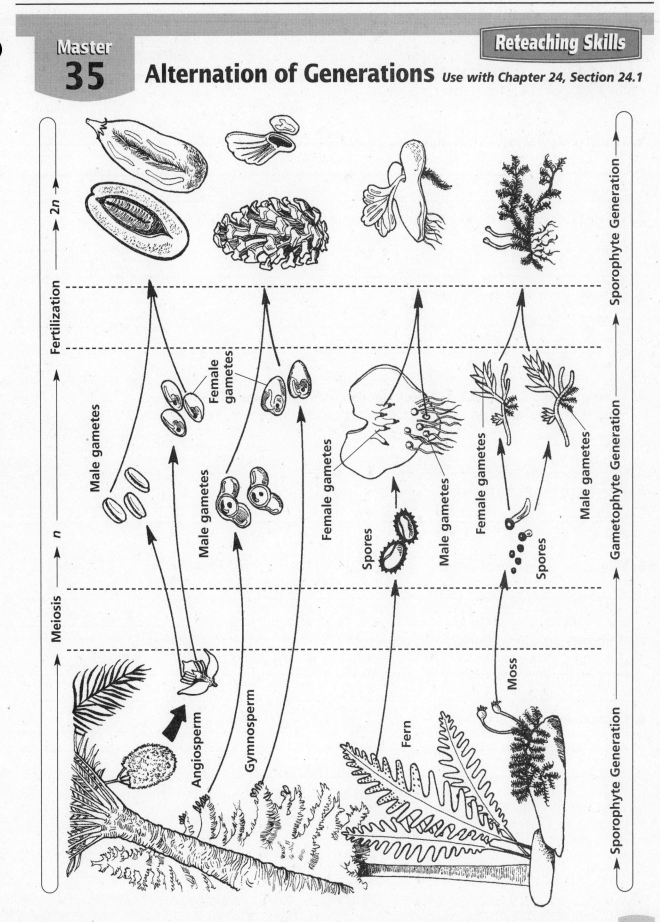

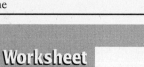

Alternation of Generations *Use with Chapter 24, Section 24.1*

1. Which process of cell division produces the spores in the sporophyte plant?

_____

_____

2. Which plant generation results from the fusion of gametes?

_____

_____

3. Describe the cells of a gametophyte.

_____

_____

_____

4. What structures are produced by fertilization in angiosperms and gymnosperms? What is the symbol for the number of chromosomes in the cells of these structures?

_____

_____

5. Which generation develops from spores?

_____

_____

6. Where are gametes produced in gymnosperms?

_____

_____

7. Where are gametes produced in angiosperms?

_____

_____

8. How do seeds and spores differ?

_____

_____

Master 36

Life Cycle of a Pine

Reteaching Skills

Use with Chapter 24, Section 24.1

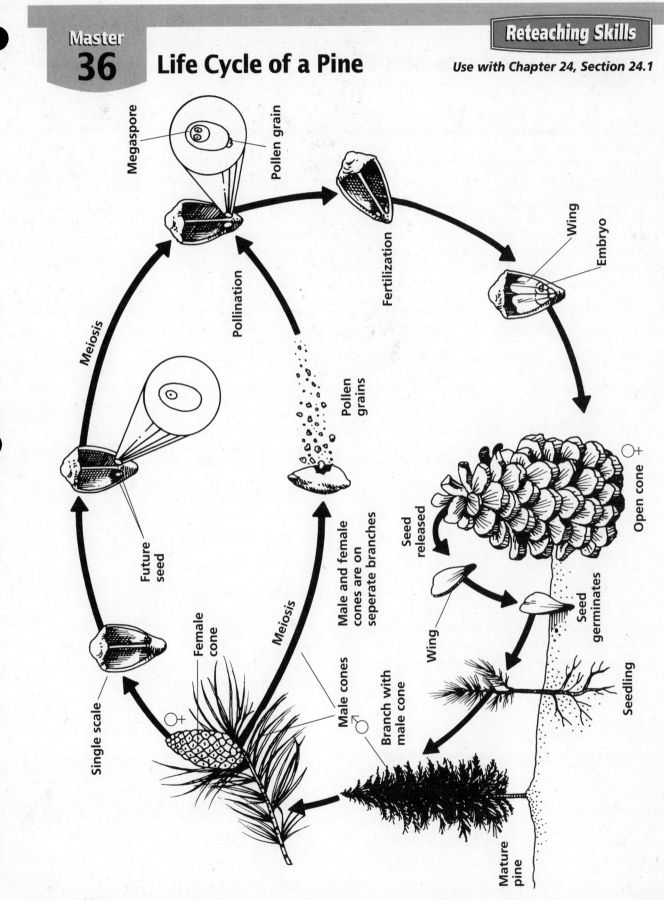

Worksheet
36 Life Cycle of a Pine

1. What are microspores and megaspores, and what is their relationship to a pollen grain and an ovule?

_____

_____

_____

2. What advantages do embryos have as a result of being enclosed in seeds?

_____

_____

3. Describe two adaptations that make it possible for conifers to survive in cold climates.

_____

_____

_____

4. What are two adaptive advantages of a tree retaining its leaves year-round?

_____

_____

_____

_____

5. Describe what happens to a pollen grain after it is blown onto a female scale.

_____

_____

_____

_____

_____

6. A pine tree is the sporophyte generation, which can produce male and female cones. Given this information, what can you infer about the cell status of the tree, that is, is it haploid or diploid? Explain your answer.

_____

_____

_____

Master
37

Fruit Formation

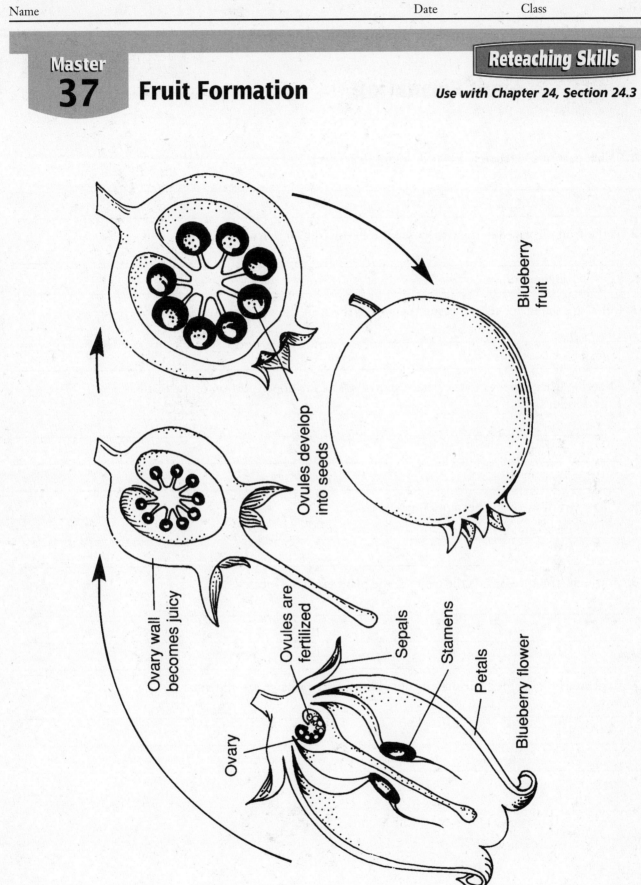

Blueberry
fruit

Ovules develop
into seeds

Ovary wall
becomes juicy

Ovules are
fertilized

Ovary

Sepals

Stamens

Petals

Blueberry flower

Worksheet 37 Fruit Formation

1. What part of a blueberry flower develops into a fruit?

_____

_____

2. Is the fruit displayed in the transparency a fleshy fruit or a dry fruit?

_____

_____

3. What are the major substances in the wall of the fruit shown in the transparency?

_____

_____

4. Describe what happens to the petals, stamens, and the upper portion of the pistil as a fruit develops.

_____

_____

_____

5. What part of the ovule becomes the seed coat?

_____

_____

6. In which structures inside the fruit are the plant embryos located?

_____

_____

_____

7. Explain why tomatoes, cucumbers, pumpkins, and eggplants are all fruits.

_____

_____

_____

Chapter

24 Reproduction in Plants

Chapter Assessment

Reviewing Vocabulary

Write the word or phrase that best completes each statement. Use these choices:

anther	pistil	stamen	germination
day-neutral plant	megaspores	ovary	petals
endosperm	microspores	micropyle	photoperiodism
protonema			

1. The response of flowering plants to the difference in the duration of light and dark periods in a day is called _____ .

2. The _____ is food-storage tissue that supports development of the embryo.

3. The _____ is the part of the flower in which ovules containing eggs are formed.

4. The _____ is a small green filament of cells that develops into either a male or a female gametophyte.

5. Leaflike, usually colorful, structures arranged in a circle around the tip of a flower stem are called _____ .

6. The beginning of the development of the embryo into a new plant is called _____ .

7. The _____ is the female structure of the flower.

8. _____ are female spores that eventually become female gametophytes.

9. The male cones have sporangia that undergo meiosis to produce males spores called _____.

10. The _____ , at the tip of the stamen, produces pollen that contains sperm.

11. The flowering time of a _____ is controlled by temperature, moisture, or other environmental factors, rather than by day length.

12. The _____ is the male reproductive structure of a flower.

13. The _____ is a tiny opening in the ovule through which a sperm cell moves through the pollen tube into the ovule.

Chapter 24 **Reproduction in Plants,** *continued*

Understanding Main Ideas (Part A)

Label the parts of a flower in the diagram below.

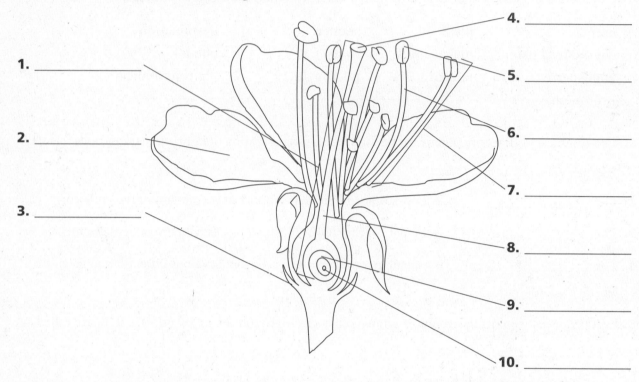

1. _____

2. _____

3. _____

4. _____

5. _____

6. _____

7. _____

8. _____

9. _____

10. _____

In the space at the left, write the letter of the word or phrase that best completes the statement or answers the question.

_____ **11.** Where does the process of double fertilization occur?

      a. in the pollen tube   **b.** in the stigma

      c. in the central nucleus   **d.** in the ovule

_____ **12.** The fertilization of the central cell produces a

      a. triploid nucleus.   **b.** zygote.

      c. diploid nucleus.   **d.** haploid egg.

_____ **13.** After fertilization, the central cell develops into the

      a. zygote.   **b.** endosperm.   **c.** pollen tube.   **d.** fruit.

_____ **14.** Which of the following plants has a prothallus that forms archegonia and antheridia and has a dominant sporophyte?

      a. mosses   **b.** ferns   **c.** conifers   **d.** flowering plants

_____ **15.** Which of the following plants produce separate male and female cones that produce microspores and megaspores that develop into male and female gametophytes?

      a. mosses   **b.** ferns   **c.** conifers   **d.** flowering plants

Understanding Main Ideas (Part B)

Answer the following questions.

1. What is the dominant generation?

_____

_____

_____

_____

2. Give at least three of the special requirements that some seeds may have before they germinate.

_____

_____

_____

_____

3. What steps are involved in fruit and seed formation?

_____

_____

_____

_____

_____

4. What is a photoperiodism? Differentiate between short-day plants and long-day plants.

_____

_____

_____

_____

_____

Chapter 24 **Reproduction in Plants,** *continued*

Thinking Critically

Answer the following questions.

1. Hypothesize why vegetative reproduction is an adaptive advantage for most plants.

_____

_____

_____

_____

_____

_____

_____

2. Flower production uses up large quantities of sugar in a plant. Sugarcane growers try to delay flowering as long as possible in order to allow time for the sugar content of the cane to increase. If sugarcane is a short-day plant, hypothesize as to how they might achieve their goal.

_____

_____

_____

_____

_____

3. Investigators tried an experiment with short-day plants in the laboratory to find out how the day/night stimulus is carried throughout the plant. Immediately after exposing the plants to light during what was normally a dark period, investigators removed all the leaves from the plant. Flowering did not occur in the plants. However, if they waited and removed the leaves several hours after the light stimulus was given, flowering did occur. Hypothesize as to the function of the leaves in the flowering process. Why did flowering occur when there was a delay before removing the leaves?

_____

_____

_____

_____

_____

_____

Applying Scientific Methods

Plant physiologists have for a number of years been investigating the stimuli that initiate flowering in plants. They have concluded that some plants are short-day plants. These plants produce flowers in early spring or late summer when days are shorter than nights. Other plants are long-day plants that bloom in summer when days are longer than nights. In still other plants, flowering is controlled by temperature, moisture, or other environmental factors.

1. How does each of these adaptations benefit the plant?

_____

_____

_____

Investigators have known about the day/night length effect on flowering for many years. However, some investigators were unsure as to whether it is the day length or the night length that actually causes flowers of a certain species to bloom.

2. Hypothesize about which of these is the stimulus that causes blooming. You must support your hypothesis with valid reasons for your choice.

_____

_____

_____

_____

_____

_____

_____

3. In planning an experiment to investigate the effect of day/night length on flowering, it is best to use plants whose flowering pattern you know. Why?

_____

_____

_____

_____

Chapter 24 **Reproduction in Plants,** *continued*

Applying Scientific Methods *continued*

4. Use either short-day or long-day plants. Plan an experiment to support your hypothesis.

_____

_____

_____

_____

_____

5. What will be your control during your experiment?

_____

_____

_____

6. What is the variable in this experiment?

_____

_____

_____

7. If the results of your experiment do *not* support your hypothesis, what would you do next?

_____

_____

_____

_____

_____

Chapter 24 Assessment
Student Recording Sheet

Use with pages 662–663 of the Student Edition

Vocabulary Review

Write the vocabulary words that match the definitions in your book.

1. _____   4. _____

2. _____   5. _____

3. _____

Understanding Key Concepts

Select the best answer from the choices given and fill in the corresponding oval.

6. Ⓐ Ⓑ Ⓒ Ⓓ   10. Ⓐ Ⓑ Ⓒ Ⓓ

7. Ⓐ Ⓑ Ⓒ Ⓓ   11. Ⓐ Ⓑ Ⓒ Ⓓ

8. Ⓐ Ⓑ Ⓒ Ⓓ   12. Ⓐ Ⓑ Ⓒ Ⓓ

9. Ⓐ Ⓑ Ⓒ Ⓓ   13. Ⓐ Ⓑ Ⓒ Ⓓ

Constructed Response

Record your answers for Questions 14–16 on a separate sheet of paper.

Thinking Critically

Record your answer for Question 17 on a separate sheet of paper.

18. **REAL WORLD BIOCHALLENGE** Follow your teacher's instructions for presenting your BioChallenge answer.

Standardized Test Practice

The Princeton Review

Part 1   Multiple Choice

Select the best answer from the choices given and fill in the corresponding oval.

19. Ⓐ Ⓑ Ⓒ Ⓓ

20. Ⓐ Ⓑ Ⓒ Ⓓ

21. Ⓐ Ⓑ Ⓒ Ⓓ

22. Ⓐ Ⓑ Ⓒ Ⓓ

23. Ⓐ Ⓑ Ⓒ Ⓓ

24. Ⓐ Ⓑ Ⓒ Ⓓ

Part 2
Constructed Response/Grid In

Record your answer for Question 25 on a separate sheet of paper.

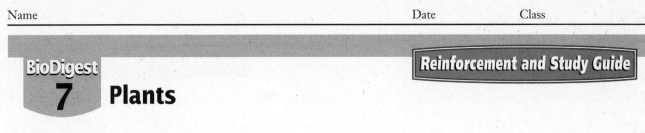

BioDigest
7 **Plants**

In your textbook, read about plants.

Study the following diagram of alternation of generations in plants. Then answer the questions.

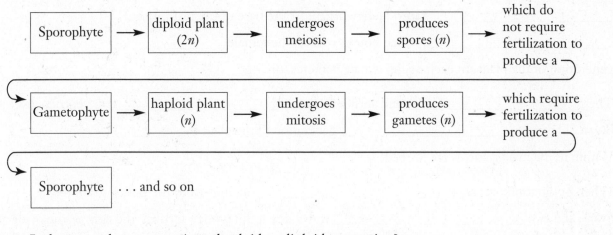

1. Is the sporophyte generation a haploid or diploid generation? _____

2. Is the gametophyte generation a haploid or diploid generation? _____

3. Is a spore haploid or diploid? _____

4. Is a gamete haploid or diploid? _____

5. Does a spore produce a gametophyte without fertilization? _____

6. Does a gamete produce a sporophyte without fertilization? _____

7. Which generation—sporophyte or gametophyte—produces a generation that is diploid?

   _____

Seed Plants

Explain how these adaptations enable conifers to survive in cold or dry climates.

8. *Needles* _____

   _____

9. *Stems* _____

   _____

10. *Flexible leaves and branches* _____

   _____

   _____

Name _____ Date _____ Class _____

BioDigest
7   Plants, *continued*

Reinforcement and Study Guide

Flowering Plants

Fill in the following blanks to explain the function of a flower.

11. A flower has two major reproductive structures. The _____ is the

_____ reproductive organ. At the base of the pistil is the

_____ , which houses ovules, the female _____

generation of the plant. In each ovule, female gametes, or _____ , form.

12. The _____ and anther form the _____ reproductive

organ. The male _____ generation of the plant is _____ .
Within it, the male gametes are formed.

13. When pollination occurs, a _____ extends from the pollen grain to the

ovary, and two _____ travel down the tube to fertilize the eggs in the ovule.

14. Some flowers are colorful and showy. Others are small and inconspicuous. Explain how these two
flower types are adapted to different pollinators.

_____

_____

_____

15. Discuss three ways that seeds may be spread through the environment.

a. _____

b. _____

c. _____

Copyright © Glencoe/McGraw-Hill, a division of The McGraw-Hill Companies, Inc.

146   BIODIGEST 7 Plants

UNIT 7

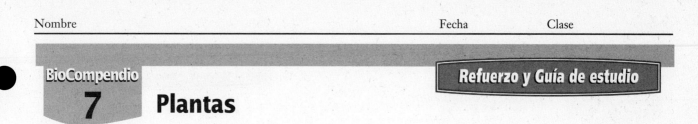

BioCompendio
7 Plantas

En tu libro de texto, lee sobre las plantas.

Estudia el siguiente diagrama sobre alternancia de generaciones en las plantas. Luego, contesta las preguntas.

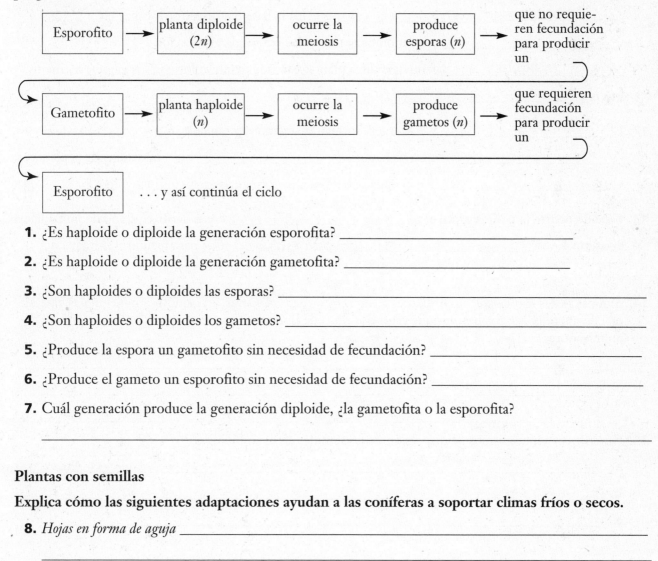

1. ¿Es haploide o diploide la generación esporofita? _____

2. ¿Es haploide o diploide la generación gametofita? _____

3. ¿Son haploides o diploides las esporas? _____

4. ¿Son haploides o diploides los gametos? _____

5. ¿Produce la espora un gametofito sin necesidad de fecundación? _____

6. ¿Produce el gameto un esporofito sin necesidad de fecundación? _____

7. Cuál generación produce la generación diploide, ¿la gametofita o la esporofita?

_____

Plantas con semillas

Explica cómo las siguientes adaptaciones ayudan a las coníferas a soportar climas fríos o secos.

8. *Hojas en forma de aguja* _____

_____

9. *Tallos* _____

_____

10. *Hojas y ramas flexibles* _____

_____

_____

BioCompendio
7
Plantas, *continuación*

Plantas con flores

Completa los siguientes párrafos que explican el funcionamiento de una flor.

11. Las flores tienen dos estructuras reproductoras principales. El _____ es el

órgano reproductor _____ . En la base del pistilo se localiza el

_____ , órgano que contiene los óvulos, la generación

_____ femenina de la planta. En cada óvulo se forman los gametos femeni-

nos o _____ .

12. El _____ y la antera forman el órgano reproductor

_____ . La generación _____ masculina de la planta es

el _____ . En el interior del polen se forman los gametos masculinos.

13. Cuando ocurre la polinización, el _____ crece desde el grano de polen hacia

el ovario y dos _____ viajan a través del tubo para fecundar el huevo del

óvulo.

14. Algunas flores son de colores brillantes y son muy atractivas. Otras, en cambio, son pequeñas y pasan
casi desapercibidas. Explica por qué estos dos tipos de flores están adaptadas a diferentes tipos de
polinizadores.

_____

_____

_____

15. Describe tres mecanismos de dispersión de las semillas en el ambiente.

    a. _____

    b. _____

    c. _____

Unit 7 Assessment
Student Recording Sheet

Standardized Test Practice

The Princeton Review

Part 1   Multiple Choice

Select the best answer from the choices given and fill in the corresponding oval.

1. Ⓐ Ⓑ Ⓒ Ⓓ
2. Ⓐ Ⓑ Ⓒ Ⓓ
3. Ⓐ Ⓑ Ⓒ Ⓓ
4. Ⓐ Ⓑ Ⓒ Ⓓ
5. Ⓐ Ⓑ Ⓒ Ⓓ
6. Ⓐ Ⓑ Ⓒ Ⓓ
7. Ⓐ Ⓑ Ⓒ Ⓓ
8. Ⓐ Ⓑ Ⓒ Ⓓ
9. Ⓐ Ⓑ Ⓒ Ⓓ

Part 2   Constructed Response/Grid In

Record your answers for Questions 10–12 on a separate sheet of paper.

Record and bubble in your answer on the grid.

13.

Contents

Unit 7
Plants
Teacher Support and Planning

Teacher Support

Chapter 21 **What is a plant?**

Identifying Characteristics of Plant Divisions

Have each student make a Foldable, using the matchbook fold shown below, to identify characteristics of the plant divisions.

How to Use the Foldable

Have students . . .

1. construct a matchbook fold. *If students need additional instructions to construct a matchbook fold, the bottom of this page can be reproduced and distributed to students.*

2. label the lower flap of the large two-tab matchbook *Plants*, the left tab *Non-seed Plants*, and the right tab *Seed Plants*.

3. write the name of a different plant division on each of the small matchbooks.

4. glue the small matchbooks inside the two-tab matchbook so that they are in the correct category.

5. trade their Foldables with a friend and quiz each other on the contents.

Going Further

- List characteristics of each plant division inside the appropriate small matchbook.

- Draw a representative of each plant division on the front of the appropriate small matchbook.

Matchbook Fold

STEP 1 **Fold** an 11 × 17 piece of paper lengthwise into thirds. **Fold** the paper widthwise into fourths. **Cut** along the folds.

STEP 2 **Fold** each small piece of paper in half. Make the back edge 1.5 cm longer than the front edge. **Fold** the tab over the front edge, creating an envelope. **Label** as instructed.

STEP 3 **Fold** another sheet of paper in half vertically. Make the back edge about 1.5 cm longer than the front edge. **Fold** the tab over the front edge, creating an envelope.

STEP 4 **Cut** the front flap in half to create two tabs. **Label** as instructed.

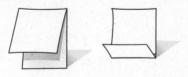

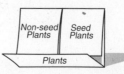

Comparing and Contrasting Monocots and Dicots

Have each student make a Foldable, using the two-tab book shown below, to compare and contrast monocots and dicots.

How to Use the Foldable

Have students . . .

1. construct a two-tab book. *If students need additional instructions to construct a two-tab book, the bottom of this page can be reproduced and distributed to students.*

2. cut the left tab in the shape of a lima bean, making sure the top fold is not completely cut.

3. cut the right tab in the shape of a corn seed, making sure the top fold is not completely cut.

4. label the lima bean *Dicot* and the corn seed *Monocot*.

5. list characteristics of each plant type under the appropriate tab.

6. use their Foldables to review monocots and dicots before the test.

Going Further

• Give examples of each plant type under the appropriate tab.

• With permission, collect, press, paste, and label common examples of dicots and monocots on separate small sheets of paper. Tape or staple these into the two-tab book.

Two-Tab Book

STEP 1 **Fold** a vertical sheet of paper in half from top to bottom.

STEP 2 **Fold** in half from side to side with the fold at the top.

STEP 3 **Unfold** the paper once. **Cut** only the fold of the top flap to make two tabs.

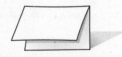

STEP 4 **Turn** the paper vertically and **cut** the front as instructed.

Chapter
23 Plant Structure and Function

Identifying Plant Structures

Have each student make a Foldable, using the three-tab book shown below, to name and identify major organs of a flowering plant.

How to Use the Foldable

Have students . . .

1. construct a three-tab book. *If students need additional instructions to construct a three-tab book, the bottom of this page can be reproduced and distributed to students.*

2. draw and label a typical flowering plant that shows roots, stems, and leaves.

3. describe the function of each plant organ on the back of the appropriate tab.

4. use their Foldables to review what they have learned about plant structures.

Going Further

• Name and describe adaptations of each organ for the environment where the student lives on the paper under the appropriate tab.

• Make cross-section diagrams of typical dicot and monocot roots and stems on the back of the Foldable.

✂ --

Three-Tab Book

STEP 1 **Fold** a vertical sheet of paper from side to side. **Draw** and **label** a typical flowering plant.

STEP 2 **Turn** lengthwise and **fold** the plant diagram into appropriate parts.

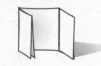

STEP 3 **Unfold** and **cut** only the top layer along both folds to make three tabs.

STEP 4 **Draw** and **label** as instructed.

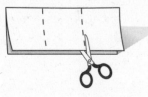

Chapter
24 Reproduction in Plants

Use with Section 24.3

Sequencing Flowering Plant Life Cycles

Have each student make a Foldable, using the pocket book shown below, to sequence the life cycle of a flowering plant.

How to Use the Foldable

Have students . . .

1. construct a pocket book. *If students need additional instructions to construct a pocket book, the bottom of this page can be reproduced and distributed to students.*

2. draw the life cycle stages of a flowering plant on separate 3×5 cards using ***Figure 24.12*** in the text as a guide.

3. label the left pocket *Haploid* and the right pocket *Diploid* and place each index card in the correct pocket.

4. trade their Foldables with a friend and quiz each other on the contents.

Going Further

- Illustrate the life cycle of a flowering plant on the front of the Foldable.

- Compare and contrast the life cycle of a flowering plant with the life cycles of mosses, ferns, and conifers.

Pocket Book

STEP 1 Fold a vertical 5-cm tab along the long edge of a sheet of paper.

STEP 2 Fold in half so the tab is on the inside.

STEP 3 Open the paper and **glue** the edges of the 5-cm tab to make a pocket. **Label** as shown.

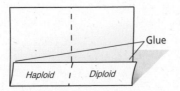

Glue

Haploid | *Diploid*

Chapter 21

MiniLab 21.1
Page 3 • Examining Land Plants

Expected Results

Students will examine a liverwort and correlate their observations on liverwort structure with adaptations of land plants.

Analysis

1. the greater the number of cells, the more water retained
2. yes; enables plant to obtain water and minerals from soil, helps anchor plant to ground
3. gas exchange; upper surface is exposed to air

MiniLab 21.2
Page 4 • Looking at Modern and Fossil Plants

Expected Results

Students will find a number of similarities and some differences between the living plants and their fossil relatives. Numbers of similarities and differences will depend on the thoroughness of student observations.

Analysis

1. Similarities—green, grow upright, have scalelike leaves. Differences—tall and thick fossil stem, short and thin living stem, leaves on top of fossil stem, ridged surface of fossil stem, leaves on living stem. Student answers on the closeness of the relationship may vary. If going by general appearance, students may agree that they are closely related. If using the total number of similarities and differences, students may disagree.
2. Similarities—green, grow upright, leaves are in whorls, leaves are small, rings on stem. Differences—fossil has branches while living is one single stem, fossil is taller and thicker, living plant leaves appear to be much smaller than fossil. Student answers on the closeness of the relationship may vary. If going by general appearance, students may agree that they are closely related. If using the total number of similarities and differences, students may disagree.

Design Your Own BioLab
Page 5 • How can you make a key for identifying conifers?

Data and Observations: Have students record their keys and turn them in at the end of class. Make transparencies of sample keys and use them in class the following day as a means for illustrating correct and incorrect key design.

Analyze and Conclude

1. By using student key design on the overhead, the entire class can determine whether or not the key works.
2. It can distinguish poisonous from nonpoisonous plants, and harmful from nonharmful insects.
3. Student key designs placed on the overhead will illustrate the diversity of student trait choices used to organize and design each key. Make sure students understand that their keys must distinguish among several similar conifers, each of which must be uniquely identified. Each fork in their key must be specific and identifiable.

Reinforcement and Study Guide
Page 7 • Section 21.1

1. What are plants?
2. What are psilophytes?
3. What are cuticles?
4. What is a leaf?
5. What is a root?
6. generations
7. gametes
8. haploid
9. sporophyte
10. diploid
11. meiosis
12. c
13. b
14. a
15. a
16. Vascular plants have long, tubelike cells that form tissues that transport food, water, and other materials. Nonvascular plants have thin tissues that allow nutrients and water to travel from one cell to another by osmosis and diffusion.
17. Seeds protect the embryos and spores protect haploid cells and keep them from drying out. Seeds have a diploid embryo with a food supply that are covered with a protective coat. Spores have a haploid cell with a hard protective covering.
18. Algae live in water and absorb dissolved substances directly into their cells. Most land plants absorb dissolved substances from the soil.

Page 9 • Section 21.2

1. c
2. e
3. b
4. a
5. d
6. Nonvascular, Non-seed Plants
7. Nonvascular, Non-seed Plants
8. Nonvascular, Non-seed Plants
9. Vascular, Non-seed Plants
10. Vascular, Non-seed Plants
11. Vascular, Non-seed Plants
12. Vascular, Non-seed Plants
13. Vascular, Seeds in Cones
14. Vascular, Seeds in Cones
15. Vascular, Seeds in Cones
16. Vascular, Seeds in Cones
17. Vascular, Seeds in Fruits
18. What are plants of the psilophyta division, or whisk ferns?
19. What are plants of the arthrophyta division, or horsetails?
20. What are plants of the hepaticophyta division, or liverworts?
21. What are spores?
22. What are plants of the bryophyta division, or mosses?
23. cycadophyta
24. ginkophyta
25. anthophyta
26. gnetophyta
27. coniferophyta

Refuerzo y Guía de estudio
Página 11 • Sección 21.1

1. ¿Qué son las plantas?
2. ¿Qué son las psilofitas?
3. ¿Qué es la cutícula?
4. ¿Qué es una hoja?
5. ¿Qué es una raíz?
6. generaciones
7. gametos
8. haploides
9. esporofita
10. diploides

11. meiosis
12. c
13. b
14. a
15. a
16. Las plantas vasculares poseen células alargadas y de forma tubular que forman tejidos para el transporte de nutrientes, agua y otros materiales. Las plantas no vasculares poseen tejidos delgados que permiten el paso de nutrientes y agua, de una célula a otra, mediante difusión y osmosis.
17. Las semillas protegen los embriones y las esporas protegen las células haploides contra la deshidratación. Las semillas contienen el embrión diploide y su alimento, el cual está cubierto por una capa protectora. Las esporas tienen una cubierta protectora dura que protege una célula haploide.
18. Las algas viven en el agua y sus células absorben directamente las sustancias disueltas. La mayoría de las plantas terrestres absorben sustancias disueltas del suelo.

Página 13 • Sección 21.2

1. c
2. e
3. b
4. a
5. d
6. no vascular; plantas sin semilla
7. no vascular; plantas sin semilla
8. no vascular; plantas sin semilla
9. vascular; plantas sin semilla
10. vascular; plantas sin semilla
11. vascular; plantas sin semilla
12. vascular; plantas sin semilla
13. vascular; semillas en conos
14. vascular; semillas en conos
15. vascular; semillas en conos
16. vascular; semillas en conos
17. vascular; semillas en frutos
18. ¿Qué son las plantas de la división psilofita?
19. ¿Qué son las plantas de la división esfenofita, también conocidas como equisetos o colas de caballo?
20. ¿Qué son las plantas de la división hepaticofita, también conocidas como hepáticas?
21. ¿Qué son las esporas?
22. ¿Qué son las plantas de la división briofita, también conocidas como musgos?

23. cicadofita
24. gingkofita
25. antofita
26. gnetofita
27. coniferofita

Concept Mapping

Page 15 • Adaptations of Land plants

Answers may vary. Possible map shown.

1. root
2. absorbs water and dissolved minerals from soil; stores starch; anchors plant
3. stem
4. supports plant; has tissues to carry food and water from one part of plant to another
5. leaf
6. organ where photosynthesis usually occurs
7. cuticle
8. reduces water loss
9. seed
10. contains embryo and food supply for growing embryo covered by protective coat

Problem Solving

Page 16 • Solving Plant Problems

1. Answers will vary. Cypress trees are conifers. They do not produce flowers. Conifers are vascular seed plants that produce seeds in cones.
2. Answers will vary. This plant is a moss. It grows in cool, moist places on dead logs or on damp rocks. It grows best outside in a park or forest but can be grown inside a terrarium.
3. Answers will vary. The plant is not a moss but a liverwort, in particular a leafy liverwort. Like mosses, liverworts grow in moist habitats. The leafy liverwort is a creeping plant with three rows of flat, thin leaves. The other type of liverwort, the thallose liverwort, has a broad body that looks like a lobed leaf.
4. Answers will vary. Club mosses do exist today, but they are much smaller. Species existing today are usually less than 25 centimeters high, but their ancestors grew as tall as 30 meters. They did form a large part of the vegetation of Paleozoic forests. The plants of these ancient forests have become coal and are now used by people for fuel.

Section Focus Transparency 50

Page 17 • Life on Land

Purpose

• To identify some adaptations of land plants

Teaching Suggestions

• Before projecting the transparency, discuss with students the moist environment in which most organisms they have already studied live. Ask students what essential role water plays in the life cycle of these organisms. (Water transports dissolved materials to and from the organism; fertilization takes place in water and embryos develop there.)

• Project the transparency, and explain that the illustration is of a prairie. Ask students what they know about prairies. (Summers are hot, winters are cold, and rainfall is uncertain. Most prairies in the United States are located in the midwest.)

• *Answers to questions on the transparency include:*

1. Answers will vary, but students might indicate that the environment is dry and receives a lot of sunshine.
2. Answers will vary, but might include: roots that absorb water and minerals, tissues to transport water and minerals throughout the plant, and chlorophyll that uses sunlight for making food.

Section Focus Transparency 51

Page 18 • Bryophytes and Hepaticophytes

Purpose

• To introduce the characteristics of bryophytes and hepaticophytes

Teaching Suggestions

• Before projecting the transparency, have students describe any mosses they have seen. Ask in what type of environment mosses grow. (moist)

• Project the transparency, and have students compare the moss and the liverwort. Explain that the leaf-like structures are not true leaves, but they do contain chlorophyll.

• *Answers to questions on the transparency include:*

1. Without vascular tissue, most mosses and liverworts are unable to live in dry habitats.
2. The lack of vascular tissue limits the size of most bryophytes and hepaticophytes because materials must move through the organism by diffusion.

Teacher Guide & Answers

Basic Concept Transparency 33
Page 19 • Phylogeny of Non-Seed Plants

Purpose
- To show the relationships among divisions of non-seed plants

Teaching Suggestions
- Explain that the age of ancient non-seed plants and their order of evolution is determined by the fossil record. Put another way, the age of a fossil can be inferred from the age of the rock in which the fossil is found. A determination of changes in fossils, from non-seed to seed plants, can contribute to determining hypothetical lines of evolution.
- Discuss the evidence supporting the idea that non-seed plants and protists may have evolved from a common ancestor or that non-seed plants evolved directly from protists. Either scenario is possible because some sort of simple photosynthetic organism must have been the ancestor of non-seed plants and/or protists.
- Obtain or borrow fossils of non-seed plants and have students try to identify the division to which the fossil belongs, using the transparency and student text as guides.

Extension: Critical Thinking
- Ask students how our present climate limits the distribution of non-seed plants. The climate is warmer and dryer than in the past. Non-seed plants must have access to water for reproduction, and their distribution is limited without it.

Answers to Student Worksheet
1. bryophytes
2. arthrophytes
3. The transparency shows that protists and non-seed plants evolved from a common ancestor.
4. whisk ferns; club mosses; horsetails; ferns
5. bryophytes, hepaticophytes, anthocerophytes
6. The lepidodendrons are ancestors of the lycophytes. Lycophytes evolved into the 1000 species.

Chapter Assessment
Page 21 • Reviewing Vocabulary

1. e
2. f
3. g
4. a
5. h

6. c
7. b
8. d
9. A nonvascular plant is a plant that lacks the vascular tissues. Water and nutrients move from cell to cell by osmosis and diffusion.
10. Vascular tissues are made up of tubelike, elongated cells through which water, food, and other materials are transported.

Page 22 • Understanding Concepts (Part A)

a. liverworts
b. hornworts
c. mosses
d. whisk ferns
e. club mosses
f. horsetails
g. ferns
h. palmlike trees with cones as long as 1 m
i. three distinct genera
j. only one living species
k. needlelike or scaly leaves
l. flowering plants

Page 23 • Understanding Concepts (Part B)

1. Both plants and green algae have cell walls that contain cellulose. Both groups have the same types of chlorophyll used in photosynthesis. Algae and plants store food in the form of starch; other organisms store food as glycogen and other sugars, and/or lipids.
2. The evolution of vascular tissue enabled plants to survive in many more habitats. Vascular plants can live farther from water than nonvascular plants. Vascular tissue also helps support upright growth and allows vascular plants to grow larger than nonvascular plants.
3. The waxy cuticle is composed of lipids, and lipids do not dissolve in water, so the cuticle helps prevent the water in plant tissues from evaporating into the atmosphere.
4. Major events that highlight the evolution of plants include origins of plants from green algae, the development of vascular tissue, the production of seeds, and the formation of flowers.
5. Both cycads and conifers produce seeds in cones. Cones are scaly structures that support male or female reproductive structures. Flowering plants, in contrast, produce seeds enclosed in a fruit.

Page 24 • *Thinking Critically*

1. Light at a wavelength of 550 nm initiates germination.
2. At 700 nm, 100 percent of the spores germinate.
3. orange and red
4. Accept any reasonable answer. Many chemical processes occur in a plant. The processes may cause a metal to combine with other substances to form a harmless compound. A test would not reveal the presence of a metal in a compound.
5. This behavior helps the moss survive during the dry period by making it inactive. It makes the moss active only at a time when conditions are right for it to grow.

Page 25 • *Applying Scientific Methods*

1. Answers will vary. Students may suggest that the sucrose somehow causes a normal haploid cell to undergo changes that double its chromosome number and make it ready to produce sporophytes.
2. Plans will vary, depending on the hypothesis. Students may vary the amount of sucrose in the medium to observe the effect on the reproductive cycle.
3. The variable may be differing amounts of sucrose in the medium.
4. The medium with no sucrose will be the control.
5. Less light will reduce the rate of photosynthesis.
6. Answers will vary but may include that gametophytes require additional nutrients in order to produce a totally different generation—the sporophyte generation. Perhaps the plants need less energy to produce another similar generation—the gametophyte generation.
7. Answers will vary but may include that such an experiment provides insights into conditions that may explain how and why alternation of generation occurs and may have applications in plant technology.

Student Recording Sheet

Page 77
Answers can be found on page 574 in the Teacher Wraparound Edition.

Chapter 22

MiniLab 22.1
Page 31 • Identifying Fern Sporangia

Expected Results

Students will see a few spores released from sporangia under water but should see many more in glycerin.

Analysis

1. Spores are more easily seen in glycerin.
2. Glycerin caused the sporangia to break open.
3. Student answers may vary—drying out of sporangium, absorption of water.
4. Student answers may vary—glycerin causes osmotic imbalance.

MiniLab 22.2
Page 32 • Comparing Seed Types

Expected Results

The lima bean, pea, and sunflower are dicots. All others are monocots. Rice and lima bean seeds will turn blue.

Analysis

1. The seeds turn purple.
2. Starch is food for a growing embryo.

Internet Biolab
Page 33 • Researching Trees on the Internet

Data and Observations: Student data tables will vary depending on the initial trees

Analyze and Conclude

1. Coniferophytes are cone-bearing trees, seeds formed on cones; anthophytes are flowering plants, seed formed within a fruit.
2. Student answers will vary. The Internet (if used) will provide information for the data table.
3. Student answers will vary. Students may select rate of growth, temperature tolerance, or disease resistance as the most important qualities.
4. a. Student answers will vary.
   b. Student answers will vary.
5. a. High summer temperature and drought tolerance would be important factors.
   b. Long periods of drought during the summer would be an important factor.
   c. Temperature tolerance during the winter would be an important factor.

Reinforcement and Study Guide
Page 35 • Section 22.1

1. water
2. gametophyte
3. antheridia, archegonia
4. rhizoids
5. an oily or a shiny surface
6. thallose, leafy
7. chloroplasts
8. mosses, liverworts, hornworts
9. b
10. c
11. c

Page 36 • Section 22.2

1. sporophyte
2. leaves
3. reproductive cells
4. strobilus
5. prothallus
6. antheridia
7. archegonia
8. Sperm
9. egg
10. Fertilization
11. zygote
12. false
13. true
14. false
15. true
16. leaves
17. sporophyte
18. gametophyte
19. rhizome, storage
20. fronds
21. pinnae
22. veins
23. club or spike mosses, horsetails, ferns
24. Sphenophytes are called scouring rushes because they contain silica, an abrasive substance, and were once used to scour cooking utensils.
25. Ferns evolved into many more species and are more abundant. Also, ferns can be found in many types of environments.

Page 38 • Section 22.3

1. embryo, cotyledons
2. seeds, gymnosperms
3. water, fertilization
4. pollen grain
5. ovule
6. two years
7. many years
8. one year or less
9. Monocotyledons, dicotyledons
10. false
11. true
12. true
13. false
14. true
15. true

Refuerzo y Guía de estudio
Página 39 • Sección 22.1

1. agua
2. gametofita
3. anteridios; arquegonios
4. rizoides
5. una superficie brillante o aceitosa
6. talosas; foliosas
7. cloroplastos
8. musgos; hepáticas; ceratófilos
9. b
10. c
11. c

Página 40 • Sección 22.2

1. esporofito
2. hojas
3. células reproductoras
4. estróbilo
5. prótalo
6. anteridio
7. arquegonio
8. espermatozoides
9. huevos
10. fecundación
11. cigoto
12. falso
13. verdadero

14. falso
15. verdadero
16. hojas
17. esporofita
18. gametofito
19. rizoma; reserva
20. frondas
21. pinas
22. nervaduras o venas
23. licopodios; colas de caballo o equisetos; helechos
24. A las esfenofitas se les conoce en inglés como "zacates para fregar" porque debido a que contienen sílice, una sustancia abrasiva, se usaron alguna vez para fregar los utensilios de cocina.
25. Porque los helechos evolucionaron en una gran variedad de especies y son más abundantes. Además, los helechos viven en una gran diversidad de ambientes.

Página 42 • Sección 22.3

1. embrión; cotiledones
2. semillas; gimnospermas
3. agua; fecundación
4. grano de polen
5. óvulo
6. dos años
7. varios años
8. un año o menos
9. monocotiledóneas; dicotiledóneas
10. falso
11. verdadero
12. verdadero
13. falso
14. verdadero
15. verdadero

Concept Mapping
Page 43 • Characteristics of Anthophyta

1. monocotyledons
2. one seed leaf
3. three
4. parallel veins
5. dicotyledons
6. two seed leaves
7. four or five
8. branched veins

Teacher Guide & Answers

Critical Thinking
Page 44 • *Distribution of* **Ginko Biloba**

1. The species covered western North America and northern Asia.
2. *Ginkgo biloba* was found in one section of northwestern North America, southern Greenland, northern and central Europe, and a portion of northeastern Asia.
3. in central Europe
4. Greenland, Iceland, and northern North America were attached to Europe and Asia at the time, so the *Ginkgo biloba* was located across the northern region of the world at the time.

Section Focus Transparency 52
Page 45 • *What's Green and Essential for Life?*

Purpose
- To generalize about the importance of plants to all life and to recognize that some plants produce seeds and others do not

Teaching Suggestions
- Project the transparency, and have students identify the plants shown. (fern, moss, apple tree, corn plant)
- Ask students why the organisms shown are all classified as plants. (All are multicellular eukaryotes; all are made of cells surrounded by a cell wall; all contain chlorophyll.)
- *Answers to questions on the transparency include:*

1. They carry out photosynthesis, using carbon dioxide and giving off oxygen, and storing chemical energy, which enters the food chain.
2. The plants at the top reproduce by spores; those at the bottom produce seeds.

Section Focus Transparency 53
Page 46 • *Plants and Their Environments*

Purpose
- To introduce that plants have different structural adaptations for living in wet and dry environments

Teaching Suggestions
- Project the transparency, and ask students to describe the structure of the these two plants. (Mosses are relatively flat plants; ferns are taller plants.)
- Review with students the structure of a moss plant.

(Mosses are small plants with leafy stems. The leaves of mosses are usually one cell thick.)
- *Answers to questions on the transparency include:*

1. Mosses live in moist environments, while ferns can be found in various environments including dry land and moist areas.
2. Mosses must grow in moist areas because their life functions require a close association with water. They do not have vascular tissue, so they are limited in size. Ferns, on the other hand, have vascular tissues, which allow them to grow tall. Water and other nutrients can be transported throughout the plant. They do not have to live in close association with water.

Section Focus Transparency 54
Page 47 • *Gymnosperm Cones*

Purpose
- To introduce the reproductive function of cones

Teaching Suggestions
- Project the transparency, and tell students that the cones shown are only a small number of the many different cones produced by different gymnosperm species.
- Tell students that gymnosperm comes from Greek root words meaning "naked" and "seed." Ask students why they think this group of plants was given this name. (The seeds produced on the cones do not have a fleshy covering like seeds enclosed in fruits.)
- *Answers to questions on the transparency include:*

1. Answers will vary, but might include the observation that they appear tough and woody and have scales.
2. The function of cones is to produce male and female reproductive structures. Also, seeds are produced in cones.

Basic Concepts Transparency 34
Page 49 • *Phylogeny of Seed Plants*

Purpose
- To show the evolutionary relationships among nonflowering seed plants, using the Geologic Time Scale

Teaching Suggestions
- Point out that nonflowering seed plants are second only to flowering plants in complexity.

- Have students discuss the various adaptations of nonflowering seed plants that have adaptive value. The discussion should include parts other than seeds, such as leaf structure and function.

- Emphasize that although there are relatively few species of nonflowering seed plants, they are a very important group both ecologically and economically.

Extension: Class Report

- Have students research a particular species of conifer found in the United States. Have students report on the importance and distribution of their species to other class members.

Answers to Student Worksheet

1. cycads and ginkgoes
2. The habitat of the cycads is exclusively tropical or subtropical. Organisms of the other divisions can survive in various habitats.
3. conifers
4. Seeds contain food supply for young plant. Embryo is protected from harsh environments by a tough seed coat. Many seeds are adapted for easy dispersal to new areas.

Basic Concepts Transparency 35
Page 51 • Phylogeny of Flowering Plants

Purpose

- To show evolutionary relationships among anthophytes on the Geologic Time Scale

Teaching Suggestions

- Explain that flowering plants are adapted to every habitat on Earth, including deserts, tropical rain forests, and parts of the Arctic and Antarctic.

- Point out that in addition to producing flowers, anthophytes are the only plants that produce fruits.

- Discuss why it is likely that anthophytes evolved from nonflowering seed plants and not the reverse. In general, more complex organisms evolve from less complex organisms, and anthophytes are more complex than nonflowering seed plants. In addition, the phylogeny of nonflowering seed plants indicates that they evolved in the Paleozoic era, which predates the evolution of anthophytes in the Mesozoic era.

Extension: Collection

- Have students make a collection of flowering plants. The genera of plants found in your local area should be included. Be sure that students are aware of protected species and that they do not collect them from parks.

Answers to Student Worksheet

1. monocots and dicots
2. four
3. Monocots include grasses that produce bamboo, sugarcane, and grains including corn, oats, rice, and wheat. Monocot plants also produce, among other things, onions and asparagus. Dicots include shrubs, trees, and plants that produce such foods as berries, apples, pears, peaches, beans, cabbage, mustard, broccoli, radish, turnip, collards, and kale.
4. Lamiaceae
5. When dissected, one seed would be found to have two seed leaves, or cotyledons. The other seed would be found to have one cotyledon. The former seed would be that of a cactus, which is a dicot, whereas the latter seed would be that of a palm, which is a monocot.
6. monocots

Chapter Assessment
Page 53 • Reviewing Vocabulary

1. j
2. d
3. c
4. h
5. b
6. i
7. a
8. e
9. f
10. g
11. Gametophytes produce two kinds of sexual reproductive structures. The antheridium is the male reproductive structure in which sperm are produced. The archegonium is the female reproductive structure in which eggs are produced.
12. These terms refer to the life spans of anthophytes. Annuals live for only a year or less. Perennials live for several years, producing flowers and seed periodically—usually once each year.

Page 54 • Understanding main Ideas (Part A)

1. b	6. a
2. b	7. d
3. a	8. b
4. c	9. b
5. d	10. d

Teacher Guide & Answers

Page 55 • Understanding main Ideas (Part B)

1. Nonvascular plants lack vascular tissue and reproduce by producing spores. They usually live in moist, cool environments. The gametophyte generation is dominant.

2. A seed contains a supply of food to nourish the young plant during the early stages of growth until its leaves develop. The embryo is protected during harsh conditions by a tough seed coat. The seed of many species are also adapted for easy dispersal to new areas, so the young plant does not have to compete with its parents for sunlight, water, soil nutrients, and living space.

3. Fruit provides additional protection for young embryos. Fruit also aids in seed dispersal. Animals may eat seeds or carry them off to store for food. Seeds that are eaten may pass through the animal's digestive system unharmed and are distributed as the animal wanders. Some fruits have structural adaptations that help disperse the seed by wind or water.

4. Because an evergreen tree never loses all of its leaves at one time, it can photosynthesize whenever favorable environmental conditions exist. Also, a plant's food reserves are not depleted each spring to produce a whole new set of leaves.

Page 56 • Thinking Critically

1.

	Age at Maximum growth	Maximum height	Height at 45 years
Fir	80	42 m	≈32 m
Spruce	80	39 m	28 m
Larch	90	30 m	22 m
Pine	85	26 m	18 m

2. Each conifer reached its maximum height at a different age. Each reached a different maximum height. Each line displays a different pattern of growth.

3. The ginkgo is classified as a gymnosperm because it produces seeds that are not protected by a fruit.

Page 57 • Applying Scientific Methods

1. Answers may vary. The growth of brackens may stifle the growth of crops in the grasslands, or the brackens might cause a problem by killing animals.

2. Hypotheses will vary but may include that the limiting factor in the growth of bracken is biotic, or something chemically produced by living organisms, rather than an environmental factor, because bracken seem able to grow under the worst physical conditions.

3. The plan for the experiment will vary, but if students decide that the limiting factor is biotic, they will most likely try to grow bracken ferns from spores in the presence of other plants, including another bracken colony.

4. The variable will be the factor students are testing for. For example, if they were testing to see which plants will allow the growth of bracken spores, they would plant the spores in the same pot with one other plant. They would also most likely choose to grow bracken spores in the same pot with a bracken colony.

5. The control will be growing the spores in a pot with no other plants.

6. You might think that the fern had a beneficial effect on the growth of the plant.

7. You would have to find out how the other plant grows without the bracken spores. You might also try growing that same kind of plant with plants other than bracken to see how it grows with other plants.

8. You might conclude that the bracken produces a chemical that inhibits the growth of the other plant.

9. You could repeat your trial or try to grow the bracken plant with still more varieties of plants to confirm your conclusion that bracken produces a chemical that inhibits the growth of other plants.

Student Recording Sheet

Page 59

Answers can be found on page 602 in the Teacher Wraparound Edition.

Chapter 23

MiniLab 23.1
Page 63 • Examining Plant Tissues

Expected Results

The stringy tissue will appear as nongreen tissue that resembles a track, or roadway. The soft tissue will appear green and cubelike in shape.

Analysis

1. tubelike, pipelike, stringlike, nongreen or colorless
2. cubelike, square cells, green in color
3. Yes. Long, narrow cells are ideal for transporting water and nutrients. Cubelike cells would be most suitable for food storage.

MiniLab 23.2
Page 64 • Observing Leaves

Expected Results

Students will find simple and compound leaves, leaves with pinnate, palmate, and parallel venation, and leaves that are opposite, alternate, and whorled.

Analysis

1. Class results will differ.
2. to identify a plant or to understand how they might be related to other plant species

Investigate BioLab
Page 65 • Determining the Number of Stomata on a Leaf

Data and Observations

• Student answers will vary. The number of stomata will be several thousand.

Analyze and Conclude

1. mathematical errors, different average numbers of stomata, different leaf sizes
2. Different plants will have different numbers of stomata per high-power field; stomata numbers are characteristic for specific plant species.
3. Saves time and energy; you do not get an actual or true count, only an approximation.
4. a. increase the number of samples
   b. calculate microscope's high-power area

Reinforcement and Study Guide
Page 67 • Section 23.1

1. h
2. b
3. j
4. e
5. l
6. f
7. n
8. q
9. m
10. d
11. i
12. k
13. c
14. g
15. a
16. p
17. o

Page 68 • Section 23.2

1. epidermis
2. endodermis
3. phloem
4. xylem
5. cortex
6. true
7. true
8. false
9. true
10. false
11. false
12. true
13. b
14. d
15. d
16. c
17. stem
18. petiole
19. extend
20. veins
21. cuticle
22. mesophyll
23. photosynthesis
24. epidermis
25. stomata
26. transpiration

Page 70 • Section 23.3

1. hormone
2. auxins
3. gibberellins
4. cytokinins
5. ethylene

6. tropism
7. nastic movement
8. small
9. true
10. auxin
11. positive
12. true
13. true
14. thigmotropism

Refuerzo y Guía de estudio
Página 71 • Sección 23.1

1. h
2. b
3. j
4. e
5. l
6. f
7. n
8. q
9. m
10. d
11. i
12. k
13. c
14. g
15. a
16. p
17. o

Página 72 • Sección 23.2

1. epidermis
2. endodermis
3. floema
4. xilema
5. corteza
6. verdadero
7. verdadero
8. falso
9. verdadero
10. falso
11. falso
12. verdadero
13. b
14. d

15. d
16. c
17. tallo
18. pecíolo
19. extienden
20. venas o nervaduras
21. cutícula
22. mesófilo
23. fotosíntesis
24. epidermis
25. estomas
26. transpiración

Página 74 • Sección 23.3

1. hormona
2. auxinas
3. giberelinas
4. citoquininas
5. etileno
6. tropismo
7. movimientos násticos
8. pequeñas
9. verdadero
10. auxina
11. positivo
12. verdadero
13. verdadero
14. tigmotropismo

Concept Mapping
Page 75 • Plant Tissues

1. dermal
2. vascular
3. ground
4. xylem
5. phloem
6. apical meristem
7. lateral meristem
8. root hair
9. guard cell
10. vascular cambium
11. cork cambium

Problem Solving
Page 76 • Using a Key to Identify Trees

1a. Simple leaf—Go to 3
1b. Compound leaf—Go to 2
2a. Palmately compound leaf—Horse chestnut
2b. Pinnately compound leaf—Hickory
3a. Veins coming from where the blade joins the petiole—Sugar maple
3b. One main vein and smaller veins along its length—Go to 4
4a. Leaves with lobes—Pin oak
4b. Leaves without lobes—Cottonwood

Section Focus Transparency 55
Page 77 • Plant Cells and Tissues

Purpose
- To introduce that plants are made up of different types of tissues and cells

Teaching Strategies
- Project the transparency, and ask students which types of tissue all of these plant parts have in common.
- Review with students that tissues are groups of cells that function together to perform an activity.
- *Answers to questions on the transparency include:*

1. dermal, vascular, ground, and meristematic tissues
2. Dermal tissue—covers and protects the plant; controls water loss; absorption of water and dissolved minerals; Vascular tissue—transports water, food, dissolved minerals, and other substances throughout the plant; Ground tissue—photosynthesis, storage, and support; Meristematic tissue—produces new cells for growth and repair

Section Focus Transparency 56
Page 78 • Angiosperm Structures

Purpose
- To introduce the main parts of an angiosperm

Teaching Suggestions
- Project the transparency, and ask students how the tree is similar to other flowering plants. (All have the same main parts—roots, stems, leaves, and flowers.)
- Ask students to provide examples of how plant structures are adapted for survival in different environments. (One example is the epiphytes, which grow on tree limbs in tropical rain forests. They do not have roots that are in the ground. They get water from the air.)

- *Answers to questions on the transparency include:*

1. The main parts are the roots, stem, leaves, and flowers.
2. Roots—anchor the plant, absorb water and dissolved minerals, store food; stem—support plant structures, transport materials throughout the plant; leaves—trap energy for photosynthesis; flowers—produce seeds

Section Focus Transparency 57
Page 79 • Plant Responses

Purpose
- To introduce that plants respond in specific ways to various stimuli

Teaching Suggestions
- Before projecting the transparency, ask students whether or not plants move. Ask them to give examples. (growth)
- Project the transparency, and ask students how this particular plant is growing. (Plant stem is growing towards the window; the roots are growing downward.)
- *Answers to questions on the transparency include:*

1. The plant is responding to the sunlight coming through the window and the pull of gravity.
2. Moving the plant with respect to the windowsill could alter the plant stem growth. The plant roots will always grow downward in response to gravity.

Basic Concepts Transparency 36
Page 81 • Functions of Stomata

Purpose
- To show the structures involved in regulating transpiration and gas exchange.

Teaching Suggestions
- Project the transparency and discuss how the three drawings illustrate homeostasis. The size of the openings of the stomata change in response to the concentration of water in plant cells or when the external environment is hot and dry. This, in turn, regulates the magnitude of transpiration, or water loss from the plant.

Teacher Guide & Answers

- Point out that carbon dioxide, which is necessary for photosynthesis, enters a plant through its stomata, while most of the water needed for photosynthesis enters via the plant's roots. Oxygen, a by-product of photosynthesis, exits the plant through the stomata. Make it clear that oxygen also enters through stomata for the plant's process of respiration.

Extension: Laboratory

- Have students design and perform experiments in which varying amounts of water are provided to identical plants. Students should use dissecting microscopes or other appropriate magnifying devices to observe and record how the plants' stomata respond to the various conditions.

Answers to Student Worksheet

1. The size changes when the internal or external environment is too dry or, alternatively, has an abundance of moisture.
2. The drawing on the far right shows a response to dry conditions. As water passes out of the guard cells into surrounding tissues, the turgor pressure drops inside the guard cells and causes them to change shape. This relaxation of the shape of the guard cells reduces the size of the stomatal pore. This conserves water by reducing water loss, or transpiration.
3. Chloroplasts are the sites for photosynthesis. A by-product of photosynthesis—oxygen—and one of the raw materials needed for this process—carbon dioxide—must exit or enter through stomata. Thus, it is efficient to have an abundance of chloroplasts near the stomatal opening.
4. As shown in the middle drawing, water enters the guard cells by osmosis. As the guard cells begin to expand, cellular fibers prevent the guard cells from expanding in width; therefore, the guard cells expand lengthwise. Because each pair of cells is attached end to end, the lengthwise expansion forces them to bow out. As a result, the pore opens, allowing excess water to evaporate through transpiration.

Basic Concepts Transparency 37
Page 83 • Leaf Structure

Purpose

- To identify the tissues of a leaf

Teaching Suggestions

- Use the transparency to show the relationship between the structures of a leaf and their functions.
- Emphasize the role that leaves play in maintaining a balance of gases in the atmosphere.
- Discuss leaf modifications and their functions.

Extension: Collection

- Have students collect leaves from monocotyledons and dicotyledons. Ask them to explain the function of leaf characteristics, such as the succulent leaves of desert plants.

Answers to Student Worksheet

1. The primary function of leaves is photosynthesis.
2. stomata
3. The cuticle is a waxy, noncellular layer that covers the epidermis and helps prevent water loss.
4. palisade mesophyll
5. Carbon dioxide enters the stomata; oxygen enters and leaves through the stomata; water leaves through the stomata.
6. vascular bundles (or veins)
7. Spongy mesophyll, which consists of loosely packed, irregularly shaped cells, permits gases to move between palisade cells and the outside of the leaf.
8. A petiole is the stalk that attaches the leaf blade to the stem. It contains the vascular tissues that extend into the leaf to form veins.

Reteaching Skills Transparency 32
Page 85 • What Is the Function of Trichomes?

Purpose

- To evaluate the adaptive value of various kinds of trichomes
- Skill: Comparing and contrasting

Teaching Suggestions

- Use this transparency in conjunction with plant tissues in the text.
- The questions related to this transparency will help with the assessment of critical thinking skills and provide an understanding of the various uses of the different kinds of trichomes. Discuss student responses to the worksheet questions in order to evaluate areas for review or enrichment.

- Show samples of the plants mentioned in the transparency or plants with similar trichomes to enhance student interest and understanding of these structures. Thyme, mint, and the stinging nettle may be easily accessible. Other silvery-leaved composites may also be available in your area.

Extension: Research Activity

- Interested students may wish to research the trichomes that produce digestive enzymes in carnivorous plants. They might find out what substances cause the discharge of enzymes in the plants. (Suitable nitrogenous substances from an insect on the leaf usually cause the secretion of digestive enzymes within an hour in Dionaea muscipula, Venus's fly trap.)

Answers to Student Worksheet

1. Because the trichome mats shade the leaf, they lower the leaf temperatures and thus reduce water loss in a desert environment.
2. Trichomes on cotton seeds can grow to 6 cm (2.5 inches) in length. They can deter insects from eating the seeds by providing a physical barrier or in some cases by trapping insects that crawl across them.
3. The strong aromas of thyme and mint might deter insects from feeding on the plants. The oils that produce these aromas might inhibit other plants, such as grasses, from growing in the same vicinity, thereby reducing competition.
4. The salt glands would allow the plant to excrete excess salt to the surface of the plant and therefore maintain homeostasis.
5. Herbivores that have once experienced stinging nettle's defense mechanism would soon learn to avoid these plants.

Reteaching Skills Transparency 33
Page 87 • Internal Structure of a Leaf

Purpose

- To discuss the functions of the parts of a leaf
- Skill: Classifying

Teaching Suggestions

- Present the transparency. Review the definitions of cuticle (Chapter 21) and xylem and phloem.
- Discuss the various ways to classify the parts of a leaf. Brainstorm with students to devise as many strategies as possible. Proposals may include structures with and without openings; structures directly involved in

photosynthesis, indirectly involved, and not involved; structures involved in protection, gas supply, fluid distribution, photosynthesis, and waste disposal; structures that receive materials, structures that deliver materials, and others. Discuss why a researcher might choose one of the methods—the system must reflect the purpose of the work, not the other way around. Point out that there is rarely only one way to classify a group of items.

Extension: Field Trip

- Take students to a botanical garden to see the variety of adaptations in leaves. Note especially the differences between leaves of tropical plants and plants native to more temperate regions. Afterwards, have students write a newspaper-style review of the tour and their findings.

Answers to Student Worksheet

1. *upper epidermis:* layer of cells on upper side of a leaf
   a. top layer of the leaf
   b. may contain stomata
2. *palisade mesophyll:* column-shaped cells with many chloroplasts
   a. cells just below upper epidermis
   b. primary site of photosynthesis
3. *vascular bundle:* bundle of vascular tissues, which transport materials into and out of the leaf
   a. location of tissues that conduct materials to and from the leaf
   b. forms the "veins" in a leaf
4. *xylem:* tubular cells joined end to end
   a. transports water and dissolved minerals upward from roots to leaves and other plant structures
   b. made of tubular cells
5. *phloem:* tubular cells joined end to end with adjacent companion cells
   a. transports sugars from the sites of photosynthesis to all parts of the plant
   b. made of tubular cells and companion cells
6. *spongy mesophyll:* loosely packed, irregularly shaped cells surrounded by air spaces, usually found on the underside of the leaf
   a. Spaces allow gases to move between palisade cells and out of the leaf.
   b. fewer chloroplasts than palisade mesophyll
7. *lower epidermis:* lower side of the leaf
   a. bottom layer or "skin" of the leaf
   b. usually contains many stomata

8. *stomata:* pores in the leaf
   a. site through which oxygen for respiration and carbon dioxide for photosynthesis enter leaf
   b. site through which water vapor and oxygen, products of photosynthesis, exit from the leaf

Reteaching Skills Transparency 34
Page 89 • A Plant's Vascular System

Purpose
- To identify the structure and function of stem and root vascular tissue
- Skill: Interpreting scientific illustrations

Teaching Suggestions
- Have students identify vascular structures before adding the overlay with labels.
- Tell students that different kinds of vascular plants have a vascular system that is basically the same. Monocotyledons and dicotyledons differ only in the organization of their vascular tissues.
- Have students identify edible stems and roots. Examples are white potatoes, sugar cane, rhubarb, and onions, which are underground modified stems, whereas sweet potatoes, yams, taro, carrots, parsnips, beets, turnips, and radishes are roots.
- Have students hypothesize how the roots of desert plants may be adapted to a dry climate. Root adaptations of desert plants include deep tap roots that can reach reservoirs of underground water as well as shallow roots that spread out over a wide area to absorb what little moisture occasionally falls on a desert.

Extension: Models
- Have students make models using clay, plastic, wood, or similar materials to demonstrate the vascular systems of monocotyledons and dicotyledons.

Answers to Student Worksheet
1. Xylem transports water and dissolved minerals upward from the roots, whereas phloem transports sugars throughout the plant.
2. in the apical meristem
3. Secondary growth occurs in the vascular cambium. This growth increases the thickness of the stem.

4. A root hair is an extension of a single epidermal cell. Root hairs absorb water and dissolved minerals from soil.
5. the pericycle
6. the endodermis
7. Cork cambium provides a tough covering for the surface of stems and roots.

Chapter Assessment
Page 91 • Reviewing Vocabulary

1. o	9. a
2. m	10. b
3. i	11. n
4. g	12. e
5. j	13. d
6. l	14. f
7. c	15. h
8. k	

Page 92 • Understanding Main Ideas (Part A)

1. d	6. c
2. c	7. d
3. a	8. root hair
4. a	9. transpiration
5. d	10. true

Page 93 • Understanding Main Ideas (Part B)

1. The xylem cells produced by the vascular cambium in the spring tend to be larger than those formed later in the growing season because there is more water available in spring. This alternation in the size of xylem cells produces a pattern of annual growth rings.
2. They weaken the connections between cellulose fibers in cell walls which allows cells to grow longer.
3. When fruit is kept in a closed container, ethylene gas builds up in the container. Ethylene gas promotes ripening.
4. Guard cells regulate the size of stomata according to the amount of water in the plant. When there is less water in tissues surrounding the guard cells, water leaves the guard cells. The guard cells become shorter and thicker, reducing the size of the pore. The smaller the pores, the less water will leave the plant.
5. The functions of a root are to anchor the plant, absorb water and dissolved minerals, and transport these materials the stem.

Page 94 • *Thinking Critically*

1. The phloem tissue was still intact above the ring. The liquid leaking out contained sugar, indicating that food made in the leaves was being carried down as far as the ring. The researcher concluded that the phloem transports food downward. Because the leaves remained healthy for a time, the researcher also concluded that xylem transports water to the leaves. Without water, the leaves would have wilted and died in only a few hours. The death of the leaves signaled that the roots, which absorb water, had died because of lack of nourishment.

2. The cactus grows in dry places. It is adapted to dry conditions and transpires much less than the other plants.

3. The initials will still be 1.5 meters above the ground. Growth in length of a plant stem occurs just below the apical meristem of the tip of the stem.

Page 95 • *Applying Scientific Methods*

1. Since the color is dissolved in the water, you would infer that the color was carried in the water upward through the stem to the leaves.

2. Answers may vary. Students may hypothesize that as temperature increases, transpiration will increase; this in turn will increase the rate of water flow upward.

3. Plans will vary. Students may set up three leafy celery stalks in colored water and place them in beakers with water at different temperatures—in ice water, in water at room temperature, and in warm water. All three beakers would be placed in sunlight.

4. Answers will vary. Students may use the celery stalk at room temperature as the control.

5. The temperature of water is the variable.

6. Hypotheses may vary. Students may hypothesize that light is needed for transpiration to take place.

7. Answers may vary. Students may place one celery stalk in the dark and another in the light to compare how fast the color rises in each stalk.

8. Answers may vary. Students may leave one celery stick in a window, allowing it to receive both light and dark as nature provides.

9. The amount of light received by the plant is the variable.

Student Recording Sheet

Page 97

Answers can be found on page 630 in the Teacher Wraparound Edition.

Chapter 24

Minilab 24.1
Page 101 • Growing Plants Asexually

Procedure
- Expected Results: All plant tissues will produce new growth. The garlic clove will show new root and stem/leaf growth. The carrot will show new leaves. The potato will show new stems and leaves.

Analysis
1. a. The experimental procedure demonstrates that different plant parts can generate new growth.
   b. New growth occurred within several days.
   c. Only one plant was used for each experimental setup.
2. Student answers may vary; they may include faster growth and that all offspring are identical to parent.

Minilab 24.2
Page 102 • Looking at Germinating Seeds

Procedure
- Expected Results: Germinating seeds have larger embryos.

Analysis
1. Labels should include cotyledon(s), embryo. Diagrams of dicot should include cotyledons, embryo, epicotyl, radicle, plumule, and hypocotyl. Diagrams of monocot should include only cotyledon and embryo.
2. Monocot has one cotyledon, small embryo, is slow to germinate, and its embryo parts are hard to differentiate. Dicot seed has two cotyledons, larger embryo, and easily seen embryo parts.

Investigate BioLab
Page 103 • Examining the Organs of a Flower

Data and Observations:
- Student diagrams, when colored properly, should show the petals and sepals as blue, pistil as red, and stamens as green.

Procedure
1. Organs will be in a multiple of 3 if a monocot, multiple of 4 or 5 if a dicot.
2. Answers will vary.

3. pollen grains in an anther; the probability of pollen landing on the stigma increases when there is a large number of pollen grains.

Reinforcement and Study Guide
Page 105 • Section 24.1
1. gametophyte, sporophyte
2. diploid
3. egg, sperm
4. vegetative reproduction
5. dominant
6. protonema
7. mitosis
8. meiosis
9. 2
10. 4
11. 5
12. 3
13. 7
14. 6
15. 1

Page 106 • Section 24.1 continued
1. The dominant stage in conifers is the sporophyte stage.
2. Adult conifers produce male and female cones on separate branches of the tree.
3. A megaspore is a female spore from which the female gametophyte can develop.
4. Microspores are male spores. The male cones have sporangia that undergo meiosis to produces microspores.
5. Microspores develop into male gametophytes, or pollen grains.
6. A micropyle is the opening of the ovule.
7. As the pollen grain matures, it produces a pollen tube that grows through the micropyle and into the ovule. A sperm nucleus from the male gametophyte is transported by the pollen tube to the egg, where fertilization takes place.
8. The ovule provides the seed coat as the mature seed is produced.
9. When conditions are favorable, the seed germinates into a new, young sporophyte—a conifer seedling.
10. The seedling will become an adult conifer sporophyte.

Page 107 • Section 24.2

1. flower
2. sepals, petals, stamens, and pistils
3. true
4. true/true
5. pistil/ovary/pistil
6. stigma
7. anther
8. petal
9. filament
10. ovary
11. ovule
12. sepal

Page 108 • Section 24.3

1. f
2. b
3. c
4. a
5. d
6. g
7. e
8. Some plants produce nectar as a food source. Some plants have bright, attractive flowers. Some flowers have a strong scent, and others have structural adaptations to attract animals (for example, some orchids resemble female wasps).
9. After fertilization, most flower parts die and seeds begin to develop. The wall of the ovule becomes the hard seed coat and inside the ovule, the zygote divides and grows into the plant embryo. The triploid central cell develops into the endosperm.
10. Accept any three of the following methods: Animals may eat the fruit containing seeds; they may spit the seeds out or the seeds may pass through their digestive systems. Some seeds have air pockets in their walls that enable them to float away on water. Still other tiny seeds are easily blown about by the wind or become attached to animal fur.

Refuerzo y Guía de estudio

Página 109 • Sección 24.1

1. gametofita; esporofita
2. diploides
3. huevo; espermatozoide
4. reproducción vegetativa

5. dominante
6. protonema
7. mitosis
8. meiosis
9. 2
10. 4
11. 5
12. 3
13. 7
14. 6
15. 1

Página 110 • Sección 24.1 continuación

1. La generación dominante de las coníferas es el esporofito.
2. Las coníferas adultas producen conos femeninos y masculinos en ramas separadas.
3. La megáspora es la espora femenina de la cual se desarrolla el gametofito femenino.
4. Las micrósporas son las esporas masculinas. Las micrósporas se producen mediante meiosis en los esporangios de los conos masculinos.
5. Las micrósporas se convierten en gametofitos masculinos o granos de polen.
6. Es una apertura en el óvulo.
7. Cuando el grano de polen madura produce un tubo polínico que crece a través del micrópilo hacia el huevo. El tubo polínico transporta el núcleo de un espermatozoide del gametofito masculino hacia el huevo, para que ocurra la fecundación.
8. El óvulo provee la cáscara a medida que la semilla madura.
9. Cuando las condiciones sean favorables, la semilla germinará y se convertirá en un esporofito joven: la plántula de una conífera.
10. La plántula se convertirá en el esporofito adulto de la conífera.

Página 111 • Sección 24.2

1. flores
2. sépalos, pétalos, estambre y pistilos
3. verdadero
4. verdadero/verdadero
5. pistilo/ovario/pistilo
6. estigma
7. antera
8. pétalo

9. filamento

10. ovario

11. óvulo

12. sépalo

Página 112 • Sección 24.3

1. f

2. b

3. c

4. a

5. d

6. g

7. e

8. Algunas plantas producen néctar que sirve de alimento a los polinizadores. Otras plantas tienen flores brillantes y atractivas. Algunas flores producen un perfume muy intenso y otras tienen adaptaciones estructurales especiales para atraer animales (por ejemplo: algunas orquídeas semejan avispas hembra).

9. Después de la fecundación, la mayoría de las partes de la flor mueren y comienza el desarrollo de la semilla. La pared (integumentos) del óvulo se convierte en la cáscara dura de la semilla. Dentro del óvulo, el cigoto se divide y se convierte en el embrión de la planta. La célula central triploide se convierte en el endospermo.

10. Acepte cualquiera de los tres siguientes métodos: Los animales pueden alimentarse de los frutos que contienen las semillas y pueden escupir o desechar las semillas. Las semillas pueden pasar a través del tracto digestivo. Algunas semillas tienen bolsas de aire en sus paredes que les permiten flotar en el agua. Hay semillas muy pequeñas que pueden ser arrastradas por el viento o que se pueden adherir al pelaje de algún animal.

Concept Mapping
Page 113 • Life Cycle of a Fern

1. sporangia

2. haploid spores

3. gametophyte (prothallus)

4. antheridia

5. archegonia

6. sperm

7. eggs

8. fertilized egg

9. diploid zygote

10. sporophyte

11. rhizome

12. fronds

13. sori

Critical Thinking
Page 114 • Reproduction in Flowering Plants

1. One of the sperm fuses with the central cell, forming the triploid nucleus that will become endosperm. The other sperm nucleus fertilizes the egg to form the diploid zygote that will become the embryo.

2. the endosperm

3. Just as flowering plants obtain nutrients from the endosperm, the embryo of the tea shrub may have been nourished by this extra fertilized egg.

4. Although the Mormon tea shrub has no fruit, flowers, or endosperm, it does possess a structure having the function of endosperm—the extra fertilized egg that nourishes the embryo.

5. The endosperm results from fertilization, as does the embryo that will become an adult plant.

6. Endosperm is a richer food source. It contains genetic material from both plant parents. Thus, it is less likely to exhibit a defect caused by a faulty gene. Also, embryo sacs are useless unless the eggs are fertilized. Because endosperm and plant embryo develop at the same time, after fertilization, no energy is wasted.

Section Focus Transparency 58
Page 115 • Fern Life Cycle

Purpose
• To introduce the dominant sporophyte as one characteristic of all vascular plants

Teaching Suggestions
• Project the transparency, and point out the gametophyte and the larger, more complex sporophyte of the fern.

• Draw attention to the flat, low-growing gametophyte. Explain that this structure is called a prothallus, and it produces the male and female structures. Sperm produced here must swim through a film of water to reach the egg. Ask students how the flat shape of the prothallus aids fertilization. (The flat surface enables water to collect on the surface.)

- *Answers to questions on the transparency include:*

  1. The sporophyte is dominant in ferns.
  2. In mosses, the gametophyte is dominant.

Section Focus Transparency 59
Page 116 • *Seed Dispersal*

Purpose

- To introduce strategies for seed dispersal

Teaching Suggestions

- Project the transparency, and identify any seeds students are unfamiliar with. (Figure A—milkweed; Figure B—berry; Figure C—maple seed; Figure D—cocklebur) Have students describe what is happening in each illustration. Then ask how each seed is being dispersed. (milkweed—wind; berry—animal; maple seed—wind; cocklebur—animal)

- Point out to students that often a seed must withstand periods of unfavorable conditions before it germinates. Ask how the structure of a seed enables it to survive these conditions. (A protective coat protects the seed from drying out; the food supply feeds the plant until it can produce its own food.)

- *Answers to questions on the transparency include:*

  1. The hairy plume of the milkweed acts like a parachute; the juicy flavor of the berry attracts birds; the propellerlike wings of the maple seed enable the wind to carry it a long distance; the barbs on the cocklebur cling to passing animals.
  2. Seed dispersal reduces the competition for minerals, sunlight, and water between the parent plant and its offspring.

Section Focus Transparency 60
Page 117 • *Pollination*

Purpose

- To introduce the concept of pollination

Teaching Suggestions

- Project the transparency, and explain to students that the Brazilian birthwort is a flowering plant that has woody vines and bad-smelling flowers.

- Explain further that this flower produces a bad odor, similar to rotting flesh, that especially attracts flies among other carrion insects. The insects enter the plant and become trapped overnight. While they are trapped, they become completely covered with

pollen. They then escape the next day as the plant withers. As they mistakenly enter another birthwort, the second flower is pollinated, while the insect has become trapped again.

- *Answers to questions on the transparency include:*

  1. This scent attracts insects that like to feed on meat. Flies are especially attracted to this plant. The insects land on the plant and become covered with pollen. As the insects continue to fly from plant to plant, pollination occurs. This involves the sperm fertilizing the egg of another plant.
  2. In addition to scent, this plant's color and shape attracts insects for pollination.

Basic Concepts Transparency 38
Page 119 • *Life Cycle of a Moss*

Purpose

- To show stages in the life cycle of a moss

Teaching Suggestions

- Explain the concept of alternation of generations as it is depicted in the transparency. Point out that, in this process, a gamete-producing generation alternates with a spore-producing generation.

- Review the difference between mitosis and meiosis. Point out that mitosis produces cells with the same number of chromosomes as the original cell, whereas meiosis produces cells with half the number of chromosomes (n). Relate this to the box in the upper right part of the transparency.

- Explain that moss plants must grow in crowded clumps to ensure that fertilization takes place.

Extension: Discussion

- Have students participate in a discussion of the importance of bryophytes. Students often fail to appreciate the ecological importance of such small and unassuming plants.

Answers to Student Worksheet

1. sperm and egg
2. The cells of a gametophyte are haploid (n), whereas those of a sporophyte are diploid (2n).
3. gametophyte
4. protonema
5. antheridium
6. archegonium
7. zygote

8. When the spore capsule bursts, very lightweight spores are ejected into the air. Air currents keep the spores aloft and transport them from one location to another, where they fall to Earth and produce new plants.

9. Moisture must be present because sperm must swim from the antheridium to the egg in the archegonium.

Basic Concepts Transparency 39
Page 121 • Life Cycle of a Fern

Purpose
- To show the alternating stages in the life cycle of a fern

Teaching Suggestions
- Discuss how a dry spell might affect a fern population. Ferns require a moist environment in order to reproduce because sperm from the antheridium need moisture to swim to the eggs in the archegonium.
- Explain that the stage of the fern life cycle generally observed by people is the sporophyte. This stage has roots, stems, and leaves.
- Although students may be familiar with relatively small ferns, point out that some ferns grow to heights of 5 meters or more, especially in the tropics. For example, ferns of the genus Cyathea have been found that are 24 meters tall and have leaves 5 meters long and stems 30 centimeters in diameter.

Extension: Demonstration
- Bring several different species of ferns to class to show the different leaf types and spore placements. You may be able to obtain these from a local florist.

Answers to Student Worksheet
1. Sori are clusters of sporangia, which produce spores. Sori are usually located on the underside of fern fronds.
2. archegonium
3. by the wind
4. A heart-shaped gametophyte called a prothallus is produced when a spore germinates.
5. On the prothallus, sperm migrate through water from the antheridium to the archegonium, where the egg is fertilized.
6. Gametophytes are haploid, small, and inconspicuous. Sporophytes are diploid, large, leafy, and conspicuous.

7. In most ferns, the stem grows underground and is called a rhizome. It is a storage stem that can support fronds.
8. When the sperm fertilizes the egg, the fern becomes diploid.

Basic Concepts Transparency 40
Page 123 • Life Cycle of a Conifer

Purpose
- To show the alternating stages in the life cycle of a conifer

Teaching Suggestions
- Discuss the adaptive value of seeds and how this accounts for the dominance of seed-producing plants on Earth today. Point out that some seeds can survive forest fires, frost, floods, droughts, and other natural disasters, thus ensuring survival of the species.
- Explain that the largest division of nonflowering seed plants is Coniferophyta, which includes pines, cedars, cypresses, firs, hemlocks, spruces, and redwoods. Point out that conifers can survive some of the harshest conditions on Earth and are found in both the coldest and the highest regions of Earth.
- Discuss the economic significance of conifers.

Extension: Field Activity
- Have students dissect female pine cones to observe the seed, wing, cone, scale, and ovuliferous scale.

Answers to Student Worksheet
1. sporophyte
2. Male cones produce pollen grains, whereas female cones produce eggs.
3. The female cone eventually produces a seed.
4. Meiosis occurs in the microspore mother cells of the male cones and in the megaspore mother cells of the female cones.
5. A pollen grain is a male gametophyte.
6. Egg and sperm cells are haploid, whereas seeds are diploid.
7. Germination is the sprouting of a seed, the first stage in the development of a mature sporophyte.
8. Fertilization can take place in the absence of water. Seeds are dispersed in many ways—by the wind, by insects, by larger animals—and can survive inhospitable conditions often found on land so that they can germinate later when conditions are favorable.

Seeds contain an embryo protected by a seed coat, as well as some form of stored food.

9. "Wings" enable the seeds to be dispersed by the wind, away from the parent tree.

Basic Concepts Transparency 41
Page 125 • Flower Structures

Purpose
• To show typical parts of a flower

Teaching Suggestions
• Have students identify the flower structures before adding the overlay with labels.

• Point out that not all flowers possess both male and female structures. For example, incomplete flowers may be exclusively male or female.

• Introduce the fact that certain species of plants can only be pollinated by a single species of animal. Discuss how human activities affecting pollinators can thus impact plant populations.

• Point out that the spur on *Delphinium* stores nectar for animals with long tongues, such as moths and butterflies.

Extension: Field Trip
• Take students on a field trip to a botanical garden. Have students examine the diversity of flower structures in various species in bloom.

Answers to Student Worksheet

1. The male structures are stamens, and the female structure is the pistil.

2. the ovary

3. A complete flower possesses four basic structures—petals, sepals, a stamen, and a pistil. In an incomplete flower, one or more of these structures is lacking. The flower in the transparency is a complete flower.

4. The stigma, style, and ovary make up a pistil; the anther and filament make up a stamen.

5. Sepals protect the flower bud from insect damage and dryness.

6. The color, scent, and nectar of flowers attracts a wide variety of animals such as insects, bats, and birds. These animals pick up pollen from the anthers in one flower and transport it to the stigma of other flowers.

7. Nonflowering seed plants depend exclusively on the wind for pollination. Flowering plants depend on a wide variety of vectors for pollination.

Basic Concepts Transparency 42
Page 127 • Life Cycle of a Flowering Plant

Purpose
• To show the alternating stages in the life of a flowering plant

Teaching Suggestions
• Have students identify the unlabeled structures before adding the overlay with the remaining labels.

• Emphasize that gametophytes in flowering plants are retained in the body of the sporophyte, as in nonflowering seed plants. Then use the transparency to highlight the features in the life cycle of a flowering plant that distinguish the division Anthophyta from other divisions of plants.

• Provide examples of seed dispersal strategies employed by a variety of plants.

• Discuss the general criteria necessary to end the dormancy of a seed. These include the presence of sufficient water and oxygen as well as favorable temperatures.

Extension: Project
• Have students study rapid cycling *Brassica rapa* to observe all stages of a flowering plant's life cycle.

Answers to Student Worksheet

1. A megaspore mother cell produces four megaspores by meiosis, and the microspore mother cells each produce four microspores by meiosis.

2. The female gametophyte consists of a haploid egg cell, a diploid central cell, and five polar nuclei all within an embryo sac.

3. A micropyle is the opening in the ovule through which sperm must pass to reach the embryo sac.

4. The male gametophyte consists of a pollen grain with a pollen tube that has two haploid sperm nuclei and a tube nucleus.

5. Double fertilization is the process in flowering plants in which one sperm fertilizes the egg and the other sperm joins with the central cell.

6. The endosperm provides food for the development of the embryo.

7. The hard seed coat develops from the wall of the ovule, the endosperm develops from the triploid

central cell, and the embryo develops from the fertilized egg.

8. A fruit consists of seeds usually enveloped in an enlarged ovary.

9. The seed absorbs water, the plant embryo begins to respire quickly, and the seed coat breaks open.

10. the sporophyte

Basic Concepts Transparency 43
Page 129 • Germination of a Bean Seed
Purpose
- To review the processes and structures associated with the germination of a bean seed

Teaching Suggestions
- Project the transparency and discuss each of the steps in seed germination. Point out that the embryo is not capable of photosynthesis until the leaves are functional. Until then, the embryo must rely on a supply of nourishment stored within the seed.

- Point out that seeds can remain dormant for long periods of time, germinating when conditions become favorable. Emphasize that dormancy periods vary from species to species but have been known to exceed thousands of years.

- Discuss how the seeds of plants are adapted to the temperature of their environments. Plant seeds in temperate zones generally germinate at moderate temperatures, whereas the seeds of arctic plants may germinate at temperatures approaching the freezing point of water.

Extension: Challenge
- Have students find out which variable—heat, light, or the presence of charcoal—stimulates chaparral seeds to germinate after a fire.

Answers to Student Worksheet
1. The first part to emerge from the seed is the radicle, which grows down into the soil and develops into the primary root.

2. The first part to emerge is the arched middle of the hypocotyl.

3. The plant obtains food stored in the cotyledons.

4. The period of inactivity, called dormancy, allows seeds to survive unfavorable environmental conditions that would destroy a young plant. The seed coat functions as a physical barrier.

5. General requirements for seed germination include having enough water to activate the embryo's

metabolism, having sufficient oxygen for respiration, and having temperatures suitable for growth of that particular species. Some seeds also need to pass through the acidic environment of an animal's digestive system in order to germinate. Others may require freezing temperatures, extensive soaking in water, exposure to fire, or certain day lengths.

6. The stimulus is gravity. The upward growth of the stems is called negative gravitropism. The downward growth of the roots is called positive gravitropism.

7. The plant might be exhibiting positive phototropism in order to obtain a maximum amount of sunlight. The source of this sunlight is on the left.

Reteaching Skills Transparency 35
Page 131 • Alternation of Generations
Purpose
- To show the alternating stages in the life cycles of plants
- Skill: Defining operationally

Teaching Suggestions
- Although the transparency does not show spore formation in angiosperms and gymnosperms, point out that, like all plants, these organisms produce spores. However, the spores are not released directly into the environment, as they are in ferns and mosses.

- Emphasize the cyclical nature of plant generations, and contrast the size and appearance of the sporophyte and gametophyte in the plant groups shown.

Extension: Collection
- Have students make a collection of the representative stages in the alternation of plant generations.

Answers to Student Worksheet
1. meiosis
2. the sporophyte generation
3. The cells of the gametophyte contain only one chromosome of each pair and are therefore called haploid.
4. seeds; 2n
5. the gametophyte generation
6. in the cones
7. in the flowers
8. A seed is diploid and contains an embryo along with a food supply. A spore is haploid and does not contain an embryo or a food supply.

Reteaching Skills Transparency 36
Page 133 • *Life Cycle of a Pine*

Purpose
- To understand the haploid and diploid phases of the pine's life cycle
- Skill: Sequencing

Teaching Suggestions
- Present the transparency and review the concepts of sporophyte (spore-producing) and gametophyte (gamete-producing) generations.
- Discuss the fact that a pine (the sporophyte generation) produces two types of cones: male and female. The male cones produce pollen grains, which are male gametophytes. The female cones produce ovules, which are female gametophytes.
- The wind blows pollen onto the scales of the female cones, and the pollen grain grows a pollen tube through the micropyle to the female egg. When the tube reaches the egg, the sperm nucleus of the pollen grain fertilizes the egg.
- The fertilized egg develops into an embryo and the mature ovule is a seed. The female cone releases the seed, which falls to the ground, and may produce a new sporophyte pine.

Extension: Reading
- Have students read and report on Oliver Sacks's *The Island of the Colorblind*, especially the second section, which is an extensive exploration of a disease on Guam that is caused by eating cycads, a primitive gymnosperm.

Answers to Student Worksheet
1. Microspores are the male spores produced by male cones. The pollen grain, which encloses the male gametophyte, is produced by microspores. Megaspores are the female spores produced by female cones. The ovule, which encloses the female gametophyte, is produced by megaspores.
2. Seeds protect the embryo, provide food for it as it develops, and provide a means of dispersal before germination.
3. The needlelike leaves of conifers are covered with a thick cuticle and have sunken stomata that help retain water in the tissues of the tree. The bark of conifers also helps reduce water loss by forming a protective covering over the stem.
4. Being evergreen enables trees to begin photosynthesis when environmental conditions are favorable, rather than waiting until new leaves are formed. It can store nutrients in the leaves and makes the tree less dependent upon nutrients in the soil to form new leaves.
5. The pollen grain produces a pollen tube to the eggs in the ovule. Then a sperm nucleus moves through the tube to the egg, and fertilization takes place.
6. The tree must be diploid since that is the only way a single structure could produce both male and female structures.

Reteaching Skills Transparency 37
Page 135 • *Fruit Formation*

Purpose
- To review the structures and development of a fruit
- Skill: Sequencing

Teaching Suggestions
- Bring in examples of dry fruits and fleshy fruits. Cut or break them open for students to observe seeds and compare internal structures.
- Show different fruits—for example, a pea pod, raspberry, and pineapple—and discuss how they may have developed.
- Point out that a coconut is a single-seeded fruit with a large mass of fibrous coating that enables the fruit to float great distances on ocean currents before coming to rest on a beach, germinating and producing a new plant.
- Explain that the word *vegetable* is not a scientific term, and many foods we think of as vegetables are actually fruits. If it has seeds, such as a tomato or a cucumber, it is a fruit.

Extension: Cooperative Learning
- Have students work in groups to research the two major categories into which scientists classify fruits: dry fruits and fleshy fruits. Then have the groups write and illustrate posters based on their research. Groups may decide to bring in examples of the different kinds of fruits and make an oral presentation about their distinguishing features. Discuss the fact that fruit type is often an identifying characteristic for a family of flowering plants.

Answers to Student Worksheet
1. The ovary develops into a fruit.
2. a fleshy fruit

3. The major substances are water and sugars.

4. These flower structures wither away.

5. the wall of the ovule

6. The plant embryos are located inside the fertilized ovule.

7. These plants are considered fruits because they are mature ovaries that contain seeds.

Chapter Assessment

Page 137 • Reviewing Vocabulary

1. photoperiodism
2. endosperm
3. ovary
4. protonema
5. petals
6. germination
7. pistil
8. Megaspores
9. microspores
10. anther
11. day-neutral plant
12. stamen
13. micropyle

Page 138 • Understanding Main Ideas (Part A)

1. pistil
2. petal
3. sepal
4. stigma
5. anther
6. filament
7. stamen
8. style
9. ovule
10. megaspore
11. d
12. a
13. b
14. b
15. c

Page 139 • Understanding Main Ideas (Part B)

1. Botanists usually refer to the bigger, more obvious plant—either the sporophyte or gametophyte—as the dominant generation. The dominant generation lives longer and can survive independently of the other generation. In most plant species, the sporophyte is the dominant plant.

2. Answers may vary. Possible answers: Some seeds germinate more readily after passing through the acid environment of an animal's digestive system. Others require a period of freezing temperatures, of extensive soaking in saltwater, or of being exposed to fire before germinating.

3. After the eggs in the ovule have been fertilized, the walls of the ovary enlarge and become fruit, and the seeds develop inside each ovule. After fertilization occurs, most of the flower parts die and the seeds begin to develop. The wall of the ovule becomes the hard seed coat. Inside the ovule, the zygote divides and grows into the plant embryo. The triploid central cell divides and develops into the endosperm.

4. Photoperiodism refers to the response of flowering plants to the difference in the duration of light and dark periods. Short-day plants are induced to flower by exposure to a long night. These are plants that usually form flower buds in the fall when the days are getting shorter and the nights are longer. Long-day plants flower when the nights are short. Some of the plants that flower during the summer, when days are longer than nights, are long-day plants.

Page 140 • Thinking Critically

1. Answers may vary. Vegetative reproduction is asexual reproduction in plants where a new plant is produced from an existing vegetative structure. Such reproduction is advantageous because only one parent is needed. Sexual reproduction may not always be possible if two parents are not available. Also, pollination in sexual reproduction often requires the presence of another organism or weather factors such as wind, whereas plants only need roots, stems, or leaves to produce offspring by vegetative reproduction.

2. Answers will vary. Growers might shine bright lights on the sugarcane fields for a few minutes each night. This would send the signal to the plant that the days are longer and the nights shorter and would cause the plant to put off flowering until later.

3. Hypotheses may vary. The leaves may produce a specific substance in response to the appropriate day/night stimulus. When the leaves are removed, the stimulus fails to reach the structure where the flowers are formed. When there is a delay before removing the leaves, the substance is produced in

the leaves and reaches the structure where the flowers form in time to cause flowering.

Page 141 • Applying Scientific Methods

1. Each adaptation helps the plant to produce flowers when the chances of being pollinated and of producing numerous seeds that will survive are optimal.

2. Students may choose either hypothesis. Reasons for their selection will vary. Those who choose day length may hypothesize that since other activities of a plant are solar-energy dependent, flowering may also depend on a certain number of hours of sunlight. Those who choose night length over day length may decide that flowering is a different process from photosynthesis and may require a certain number of hours a day when the plant is not engaged in photosynthesis in order to produce its flowers.

3. Knowing how many hours of daylight and darkness there are at the time when these flowers usually bloom will help you to narrow the investigation to controlling for those day/night lengths only.

4. Plans will vary but should regulate light and dark periods for growing only short-day or long-day plants. Students may change the hours of daylight and darkness by covering plants for a time to shorten the day or by providing intense light during brief periods at night.

5. plants of the same species in which the day/night length is not regulated

6. The variable is the amount of light or darkness available to the plant.

7. Answers may vary. The procedure could be checked for possible errors, resulting in incorrect results. The procedure could be repeated to support the original data. If the data remains consistent, then a new hypothesis could be developed and a new experimental procedure designed.

Student Recording Sheet

Page 143

Answers can be found on page 662 in the Teacher Wraparound Edition.

Unit 7 BioDigest

Reinforcement and Study Guide
Page 145 • *Plants*

1. diploid (2*n*)
2. haploid (*n*)
3. haploid (*n*)
4. haploid (*n*)
5. yes
6. no
7. gametophyte
8. compact shape, thick waxy covering that helps reduce evaporation and conserve water
9. thick layer of bark that insulates the tissue inside
10. bend under weight of snow and ice, allowing buildup to slide off before it becomes heavy enough to break the branch
11. pistil, female, ovary, gametophyte, egg cells
12. stamen, male, gametophyte, pollen
13. pollen tube, sperm nuclei
14. Flowers that are colorful attract birds, insects, or other animals that are in search of nectar or pollen. Flowers that lack petals such as those in tree catkins and grasses are pollinated by the wind.
15. Students can choose from four methods: seeds can be dispersed by the wind, eaten and dropped by animals, floated away on water, or carried by animals because of tiny hooks or barbs that catch upon the animals' fur.

BioCompendio 7

Refuerzo y Guía de estudio
Página 109

1. diploide (2*n*)
2. haploides (*n*)
3. haploides (*n*)
4. haploides (*n*)
5. sí
6. no
7. gametofita
8. La forma compacta y la gruesa cubierta cerosa ayudan a reducir la evaporación y, en consecuencia, a conservar agua.
9. La gruesa corteza aísla los tejidos internos.

10. Se doblan ante el peso de la nieve y del hielo, de modo que la nieve acumulada se resbala hacia el suelo, antes de que su peso rompa las ramas.
11. pistilo; femenino; ovario; gametofita; huevos
12. estambre; masculino; gametofita; polen
13. tubo polínico; núcleo del espermatozoide
14. Las flores de colores brillantes atraen aves, insectos y otros animales que buscan néctar o polen. Las flores que carecen de pétalos como las de los pastos y los amentos son polinizadas por el viento.
15. Los estudiantes pueden escoger entre cuatro métodos: el viento puede dispersar las semillas; los animales pueden comerse y defecar las semillas sobre el suelo; pueden flotar en el agua; o los animales pueden transportarlas porque las semillas poseen pequeños ganchos o espinas que se enredan en el pelaje de los animales.

Student Recording Sheet

Page 149

Answers can be found on page 668 in the Teacher Wraparound Edition.

Table of Contents

Unit 1 Heritage

Unit 2 Energy at Work

Unit 3 Making a New Nation

Name _____ Date _____

Root Words

Focus

Many words contain **root words** that come from languages other than English. For example, *bicycle* and *recycle* both contain the Greek root *cycl,* which means "circle." Knowing the meaning of a root can help you learn the meanings of words that use the same root. However, a word's literal meaning is often different from a word's common English meaning. *Cyclone* literally means "to go around in a circle." Its actual meaning is "a storm of winds that revolve around a center, such as a tornado."

Practice

Each word is followed by its root word and the root's definition. Choose two words from the box that use the same root word, and write them on the lines.

thermal	enact	produce	thermostat
dislocate	locate	react	conduct

1. education; root word *duc,* meaning "to lead"

_____   _____

2. action; root word *act,* meaning "to do"

_____   _____

3. location; root word *loc,* meaning "place"

_____   _____

4. thermometer; root word *therm,* meaning "heat"

_____   _____

Apply — Each word below is followed by a literal definition. Use a dictionary to find its actual definition, and then use the word in a sentence.

5. allocate = to place

_____

_____

6. activate = to drive or do

_____

_____

7. egocentric = oneself being the center

_____

_____

8. aqueduct = to lead water

_____

_____

Name _____ Date _____

Selection Vocabulary

Focus

propped (propt) *adj.* supported by something under or against (page 24)

edible (ed' • ə • bəl) *adj.* fit or safe to eat (page 27)

lingered (lin' • gərd) *v.* past tense of **linger:** to be slow in leaving (page 28)

inspired (in • spīrd') *v.* influenced (page 29)

unjustly (un • just' • lē) *adv.* unfairly (page 30)

persecuted (pûr' • si • kūt' • əd) *v.* past tense of **persecute:** to treat in a cruel and unjust way (page 30)

logic (lo' • jik) *n.* a way of thinking about something (page 31)

apparently (ə • par' • ənt • lē) *adv.* as far as one can judge by the way things appear (page 33)

assumed (ə • sōōmd') *v.* past tense of **assume:** to take for granted (page 34)

reality (rē • al' • i • tē) *n.* something actual or real (page 34)

Practice Write the vocabulary word next to the group of words that have a similar meaning.

1. without cause; unfairly; unequally _____

2. thought; judgement; reason _____

3. encouraged; motivated; uplifted _____

4. seemingly; evidently _____

5. actuality; fact; existence _____

6. delayed; lagged _____

7. tormented; mistreated; wronged _____

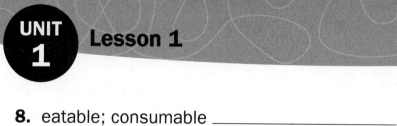
8. eatable; consumable _____

9. supposed; presumed _____

10. supported; up against _____

Apply Fill in each blank with a word from the word box that best completes each sentence.

lingered	unjustly	reality	assumed	apparently
logic	propped	edible	persecuted	inspired

11. Mr. Sheer _____ we had studied for the test.

12. This is _____ the tallest hill in the city.

13. I _____ up my sprained ankle on the chair.

14. The meat was left out all night and is no longer _____.

15. We will have to use _____ to solve this puzzle!

16. The crowd _____ taunted the visiting team.

17. The _____ is that we cannot afford a new car.

18. Kristy had the thought that her brother was _____ by the bullies at school.

19. The speech _____ the entire class to stand up and clap.

20. Because she did not want to leave, she _____ by the door.

Name _____ **Date** _____

Author's Point of View

Focus

Writers must decide from whose point of view they will tell a story.

- **First-person point of view** is told through the eyes of a character in the story. First-person narrators use words such as *I, me, we, us, our,* and *my.*

- **Third-person point of view** is told through the eyes of a narrator who is outside the story. Third-person narrators use words such as *he, she, her, them, theirs, his,* and *hers.*

 **Practice**   **Read the following paragraph from "The Land I Lost: Adventures of a Boy in Vietnam." Decide whether the author used a first-person point of view or a third-person point of view. Then, rewrite the paragraph using the opposite point of view.**

1. "My father, like most of the villagers, was a farmer and a hunter, depending upon the season. But he also had a college education, so in the evenings he helped to teach other children in our hamlet, for it was too small to afford a professional schoolteacher."

Point of view: _____

New Paragraph: _____

_____

_____

_____

_____

_____

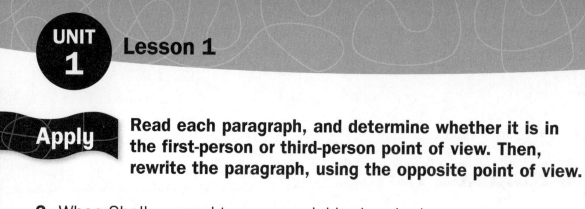

UNIT 1 Lesson 1

Apply Read each paragraph, and determine whether it is in the first-person or third-person point of view. Then, rewrite the paragraph, using the opposite point of view.

2. When Shelly moved to a new neighborhood, she was not sure she liked the kids who lived there, but when she got an invitation to her next-door neighbor's birthday party, she made several new friends.

Point of view: _____

New Paragraph: _____

_____

_____

_____

_____

3. "Never in my wildest dreams did I expect to see you here!" shouted Andy in surprise. I just stood up and smiled. It was good to see Andy after so many months.

Point of view: _____

New Paragraph: _____

_____

_____

_____

_____

Name _____ Date _____

Recording Concept Information

As I read the selection, this is what I added to my understanding of heritage.

- "The Land I Lost: Adventures of a Boy in Vietnam" by Huynh Quang Nhuong

_____

_____

- "Our Song" by Angela Johnson

_____

_____

- "The Dancing Bird of Paradise" by Renee S. Sanford

_____

_____

- "From Miss Ida's Porch" by Sandra Belton

_____

_____

- "In Two Worlds: A Yup'ik Eskimo Family" by Aylette Jenness and Alice Rivers

_____

_____

Knowledge about Heritage

- This is what I know about heritage before reading the unit.

_____

_____

_____

_____

_____

_____

- These are some things about heritage that I would like to talk about and understand better.

_____

_____

_____

_____

_____

_____

Reminder: I should read this page again when I get to the end of the unit to see how much my ideas about heritage have changed.

Name _____ **Date** _____

Ideas about Heritage

Of the ideas discussed in class about heritage, these are the
ones I found most interesting.

_____

_____

_____

_____

_____

_____

_____

_____

_____

_____

_____

_____

_____

_____

_____

Ideas about Heritage (continued)

Write down the ideas you found most interesting about the selection "The Land I Lost: Adventures of a Boy in Vietnam." Discuss your ideas with the class.

Name _____ Date _____

Writing a List

Think

Audience: Who will read your list?

_____

Purpose: What is your reason for making a list?

_____

Prewriting

Using the lines below, brainstorm five topic ideas for a story about an accomplishment of one of your family members. Then, choose one idea and write a pro and a con about using it for your topic.

Idea #1 _____

_____

Idea #2 _____

_____

Idea #3 _____

_____

Idea #4 _____

_____

Idea #5 _____

_____

Pro: _____

_____

Con: _____

_____

Revising   Use this checklist to revise your list.

- ☐ Do the ideas in your list follow the writing assignment?
- ☐ Have you made a second list of pros and cons for each topic idea?
- ☐ Have you worked with others, sharing your list to get feedback about your ideas?
- ☐ Have you decided which suggestions you will follow and which ones you will disregard?

Editing/Proofreading   Use this checklist to correct mistakes.

- ☐ Are any words misused or repeated?
- ☐ Have you checked for mistakes in spelling or capitalization?
- ☐ Have you capitalized proper nouns, literary titles, nationalities, ethnicities, languages, and geographic names and places?

Publishing   Use this checklist to prepare your list for publication.

- ☐ Brainstorm possible publication methods with your group.
- ☐ Share your list with the class.

Name _____   **Date** _____

Spelling

Focus

- **Compound words** consist of two smaller words that have been combined to form one larger word. These two words keep the same spelling in the compound word.

- **Root words** were formed from words of other languages, such as Greek and Latin. Understanding and identifying root words and their meanings can help you spell many new words. Here are some roots in the spelling words and their meanings:

  sol = alone   **scop** = to see   **stella** = star

Word List

1. skateboard
2. rattlesnake
3. mountainside
4. solo
5. telescope
6. peppermint
7. solitary
8. outstanding
9. constellation
10. stellar
11. desolate
12. solitude
13. underground
14. periscope
15. earthquake
16. breakfast
17. scope
18. sweatshirt
19. microscope
20. thunderstorm

Practice   The following compound words are missing one of their base words. Write the missing word on the line.

1. _____ snake

2. out_____

3. _____ board

4. _____ fast

5. thunder_____

6. _____ mint

7. _____ ground

8. mountain_____

9. _____ quake

10. sweat_____

Fill in the appropriate root word and write the resulting spelling word on the line.

11. _____itary   _____

12. tele_____e   _____

13. con_____tion   _____

14. de_____ate   _____

15. micro_____e   _____

16. _____itude   _____

17. peri_____e   _____

18. _____o   _____

19. _____r   _____

20. _____e   _____

Apply On the line, write the spelling word that contains one of the base words in the following compound words

21. rainstorm   _____

22. underwater   _____

23. surfboard   _____

24. sideways   _____

25. outdoors   _____

26. earthworm   _____

27. spearmint   _____

28. shirtsleeves _____

Name _____   Date _____

Common Nouns and Proper Nouns

Focus

Nouns name people, places, or things.

- A **common noun** is used to name a general, or nonspecific, person, place, or thing.
  - teacher, library

- A **proper noun** is used to name a particular, or specific, person, place, or thing.
  - Ms. Alvarez, Cook County Library

Practice   **Circle the nouns in the following sentences.**

1. For nearly eighty years, Pluto was known as the ninth planet in our solar system.

2. Clyde Tombaugh discovered the tiny frozen sphere in 1930.

3. Recently, though, scientists have decided that Pluto is too small to be labeled a planet.

4. Planets like Earth, Mars, or Jupiter are much larger than Pluto.

5. Pluto is now officially known as a *dwarf planet*.

Apply Each pair of words below should include a common noun followed by a related proper noun. For example, *book* might be followed by *My Side of the Mountain.* Fill in the missing half of each pair below.

Common Noun	Proper Noun
6. _____	France
7. former president	_____
8. river	_____
9. _____	Mt. Rainier
10. student	_____
11. _____	Saturday
12. _____	Uncle Ricardo
13. city	_____
14. school	_____
15. _____	Memorial Day

Name _____ Date _____

Prefixes *tele-* and *dis-*

- The prefix **tele-** means "far." Adding *tele-* to a base or root word changes its meaning. For example, *vision* is the ability to see; *television* is the device used to receive images broadcast over long distances.

- The prefix **dis-** means "not" or "the opposite of." Adding *dis-* to a base word often creates an antonym, or a word with the opposite meaning. For example, *disagree* is an antonym for *agree; disadvantage* means the opposite of *advantage.*

Add the prefix *tele-* or the prefix *dis-* to each base word below, and then write the new word's definition on the line. Use a dictionary if you need help.

1. content _____

_____

2. conference _____

_____

3. comfort _____

_____

4. communication _____

_____

5. continuous _____

_____

Apply Five base or root words and their meanings are given below. Add the prefix *dis-* or the prefix *tele-* to each base or root word, and then use the new word correctly in a sentence. Remember that a word's literal meaning is often different from its actual meaning.

6. connected = joined _____

_____

_____

7. phone = device for transmitting sound _____

_____

_____

8. photo = picture of a person or thing _____

_____

_____

9. scope = extent or range of view _____

_____

_____

10. approved = agreed to _____

_____

_____

Name _____ Date _____

Selection Vocabulary

Focus

Senegal (Sen' • i • gôl) *n.* a country in Africa (page 44)

lavender (la' • vən • dər) *n.* a plant with fragrant purple flowers (page 47)

delicate (de' • li • kət) *adj.* small or dainty (page 48)

ship (ship) *v.* to send by ship, train, truck, or airplane (page 50)

traders (trā' • dərz) *n.* plural of **trader:** a person who buys and sells things as a business (page 51)

surrounded (sə • round' • əd) *v.* past tense of **surround:** to be on all sides (page 51)

mist (mist) *n.* a cloud of tiny drops of water or other liquid in the air; fog (page 53)

ignores (ig • norz') *v.* pays no attention to (page 53)

quivers (kwi' • vərz) *v.* shakes slightly (page 54)

Practice **Write the vocabulary word that best matches the underlined word or phrase in each sentence below.**

1. The six of us <u>were on all sides</u> of the kitten as it played

with a piece of string. _____

2. A field of <u>fragrant purple flowers</u> filled the countryside with

a pleasant scent. _____

3. At the toy convention, hundreds of <u>people who buy and sell</u>

had set up booths. _____

4. My dog's entire body <u>shakes slightly</u> when he knows he is

about to get a treat. _____

5. The patrons were cooled by <u>drops of water in the air</u> drifting

   from a nearby fountain. _____

6. We need to <u>send</u> these supplies by airplane, or they will

   not arrive in time. _____

7. When the train passes by her apartment, Natalie <u>pays no</u>

   <u>attention</u> to the noise. _____

8. After he bumped the table in the museum, Paul broke the

   <u>small and dainty</u> vase. _____

9. His family is from <u>a country in Africa.</u> _____

Apply **Draw a line to match each word on the left to its definition on the right.**

10. mist   **a.** shakes slightly

11. ship   **b.** small or dainty

12. ignores   **c.** a plant with fragrant purple flowers

13. lavender   **d.** to send by ship, train, truck, or airplane

14. surrounded   **e.** was on all sides

15. quivers   **f.** a cloud of tiny drops of water in the air; fog

16. delicate   **g.** pays no attention to

Name _____ **Date** _____

Formulating Questions and Problems

A good question or problem to investigate:

_____

_____

_____

_____

_____

_____

Why this is an interesting question or problem:

_____

_____

_____

_____

_____

_____

Some other things I wonder about this question or problem:

_____

_____

_____

_____

_____

Formulating Questions and Problems (continued)

My investigation group's question or problem:

_____

_____

_____

_____

_____

What our investigation will contribute to the rest of the class:

_____

_____

_____

_____

_____

Some other things I wonder about this question or problem:

_____

_____

_____

_____

_____

_____

Name _____ Date _____

Writing a Summary: One Text

Think

Audience: Who will read your summary?

_____

Purpose: What is your reason for writing a summary?

_____

Prewriting Summarizing can help you study by making the text easier to understand. Summaries can also tell others about what you have read. Choose one page from "Our Song," and reread it. On the lines provided, write three ideas or events from the page you chose.

Page: _____

Idea/Event #1: _____

_____

Idea/Event #2: _____

_____

Idea/Event #3: _____

_____

What is the page's main idea or event?

_____

On a separate sheet of paper, write a short paragraph summarizing the page you read.

Revising
Use this checklist to revise your summary.

☐ Does your summary have a main idea?

☐ Is your main idea a single sentence that describes the story?

☐ Do your details support the main idea?

☐ Are your details told in an order that makes sense?

Editing/Proofreading
Use this checklist to correct mistakes.

☐ Have you checked the spellings of proper names against the original text?

☐ Have you used correct punctuation for each sentence?

☐ Have you checked for spelling errors?

☐ Have you used correct sentence structure, including subject and predicate?

Publishing
Use this checklist to publish your summary.

☐ Print or neatly rewrite your summary.

☐ Share your summary with the class.

Name _____ Date _____

Spelling

Focus

• A prefix changes the meaning of the base word it precedes. Identifying prefixes and understanding their meanings can help you figure out the meaning and spelling of a difficult or unfamiliar word. The prefix **tele-** means "far," or "at a distance." The prefix **dis-** means "not or not having". It negates the meanings of the base word. These prefixes do not change the spellings of the base words.

• **Root words** were formed from words of other languages, such as Greek and Latin. Understanding and identifying root words and their meanings can help you spell many new words. Here are some roots in the spelling words and their meanings:
graph = write; **imag** = likeness;
phon = sound; **vis** = see; **photo** = light;
gram = letter, written; **nat** = born;
ord or **ordin** = order; rank

Word List
1. disorder
2. telegraph
3. image
4. imagination
5. nationality
6. telephone
7. dishonest
8. television
9. disadvantage
10. disagree
11. telephoto
12. national
13. imagine
14. nation
15. telecast
16. discontinue
17. nationalize
18. telegram
19. imaginary
20. international

Practice

On the lines, write all of the spelling words that contain the same root or base word as each of the following words. Some words will have more than one answer.

1. native

_____

2. unimaginative

_____

3. autograph

_____

4. visual

_____

5. grammar

_____

6. symphony

_____

7. ordinary

_____

8. recast

_____

9. continuation

_____

10. agreement

_____

11. photograph

_____

12. advantageous

_____

13. honesty

_____

Apply Add the prefix *tele-* or *dis-* to each of the following base words to create one of the spelling words and write it on the line.

14. gram _____

15. cast _____

16. order _____

17. agree _____

18. honest _____

19. continue _____

20. graph _____

21. advantage _____

22. phone _____

Name _____ Date _____

Subjects, Predicates, and Simple Sentences

Focus A **simple sentence** contains only one independent clause with a subject and a predicate.

- The **subject** is the part of the sentence that tells who or what.

- The **predicate** is the part of the sentence that describes or tells what the subject does.

- A **simple subject** is the key noun or pronoun in a simple sentence that does something or is described.

- A **compound subject** is two or more simple subjects linked by a conjunction.

- The **predicate** in a simple sentence can also be simple or compound.

- **The students** visited a nature preserve.

- The students **visited a nature preserve.**

- The **students** visited a nature preserve.

- The **students** <u>and</u> their **teacher** visited a nature preserve.

- The students **visited a nature preserve** <u>and</u> **had a picnic.**

Practice The following sentences are simple sentences. Circle the subject and underline the predicate in each sentence.

1. Griots are traveling musicians and poets.

2. They play an important role in West African culture.

3. The history and traditions of West African people were shared by word of mouth for many centuries.

4. The griots' songs and poems helped keep the stories alive.

5. The stories helped preserve the culture's rich heritage.

Apply   Identify the subject and predicate in each sentence below. Then, label each subject *S* for simple or *C* for compound. Do the same for each predicate. Write an *S* next to each sentence that is a simple sentence.

6. _____ Subject: _____ Predicate: _____
Because they love the sport, Lauren and Jackie play softball every other Saturday.

7. _____ Subject: _____ Predicate: _____
Their team won six games and lost three last year.

8. _____ Subject: _____ Predicate: _____
Mrs. Suarez and her son, Will, have attended every game and several practices.

9. _____ Subject: _____ Predicate: _____
Because they are polite, they bring sandwiches for everyone after the game.

10. _____ Subject: _____ Predicate: _____
Jackie sprained her ankle and missed two games at the start of this season.

11. _____ Subject: _____ Predicate: _____
She and a team member collided and knocked each other to the ground.

12. _____ Subject: _____ Predicate: _____
Lauren played Jackie's position at first base for the next two games.

Name _____ Date _____

Multiple-Meaning Words, the Prefix *un-*, and the Prefix *en-*

Focus

- **Multiple-meaning words** are words with more than one meaning, but the same word origin. You will often need to look at context clues to figure out which meaning is being used.
- The prefix **un-** means "not or the opposite of." For example, the word *unbalanced* means "not balanced or in disorder."
- The prefix **en-** means "to put into," or "to cause to be." For example, *ensure* means "to cause to be sure."

Practice

Each word below uses the prefix *en-* or *un-*. Use your knowledge of the base word's meaning to write an original sentence for each word. Identify the base words that are multiple-meaning words and provide two definitions for each word.

1. *entangle* _____

_____

2. *encircle* _____

_____

_____

3. *unfair* _____

_____

_____

4. *uncomfortable* _____

_____

 The following sentences contain multiple-meaning words. The words and their possible meanings follow the sentence. Circle the letter of the meaning that is used in the sentence. If the prefix *en-* or *un-* can be added to the word, then add the prefix and write the definition of the resulting word on the line.

In the <u>center</u> of the <u>case,</u> there was an emblem representing the owner.

5. center
   a. the middle part
   b. a building used for a particular function

_____

6. case
   a. an instance or occurrence
   b. small, portable container

_____

Though Tim had a good <u>excuse</u> for his absence, we were still <u>forced</u> to abruptly cancel the event.

7. excuse
   a. apology or to try to remove blame from
   b. to allow to leave

_____

8. forced
   a. compelled
   b. power or strength

_____

Name _____ Date _____

Selection Vocabulary

Focus

kimono (ki • mō' • nə) *n.* a loose robe that is tied with a sash (page 64)

phonograph (fō' • nə • graf') *n.* an instrument that reproduces sound from records (page 64)

startled (stär' • tld) *adj.* excited by sudden surprise or alarm (page 66)

internment (in • tûrn' • mənt) *adj.* confined or impounded, especially during a time of war (page 68)

barrack (bar' • ək) *adj.* providing temporary housing; very plain and uniform (page 69)

sweltered (swel' • tərd) *v.* past tense of **swelter**: to suffer, sweat, or become faint from heat (page 69)

ascend (ə • send') *v.* to climb (page 71)

donned (dond) *v.* past tense of **don**: to put on (page 72)

soloed (sōl' • ōd) *v.* past tense of **solo**: to dance or perform alone (page 72)

enrich (en • rich') *v.* to make better by adding something (page 73)

Practice Circle the word in parentheses that best completes each sentence.

1. My dad replaced his (barrack, phonograph) with a CD player years ago.

2. Heather (soloed, donned) a hat and gloves before heading out into the cold.

3. The hikers (sweltered, startled) under the punishing desert sun.

4. The crowd cheered as the guitarist (startled, soloed) during the last half of the song.

5. The festival begins when the hot-air balloons (ascend, enrich) into the sky.

6. A server wearing a (barrack, kimono) served us sushi.

7. The sailors were (startled, sweltered) by a sudden wave that crashed against the boat.

8. Julio used slides to (enrich, phonograph) his presentation.

9. The (kimono, barrack) apartments provided shelter for many families escaping the flood.

10. The (internment, startled) camp was the home for many families during World War II.

Apply Write the word from the box that matches each definition below.

| barrack | phonograph | donned | ascend | enrich |
| soloed | kimono | internment | sweltered | startled |

11. _____ confined or impounded

12. _____ to make better by adding something

13. _____ an instrument that reproduces sound from records

14. _____ suffered or became faint from heat

15. _____ a loose robe that is tied with a sash

16. _____ providing very plain temporary housing

17. _____ put on

18. _____ danced or performed alone

19. _____ excited by sudden surprise

20. _____ to climb

Name _____ Date _____

Making Inferences

Focus   Writers often do not include every detail about a character or an event in the story. Readers must use clues from the text to make inferences in order to complete the picture. **Making inferences** means using the writer's clues and your own prior knowledge and experiences to develop a better understanding of the character or event.

   **Read the following sentences from "The Dancing Bird of Paradise." Make an inference about Sahomi based on each sentence and write it on the line.**

1. "Twenty minutes was all [Sahomi] had alone with her teacher, but she stayed much longer each afternoon, watching and copying the other students, learning their dances as well as her own."

   Inference: _____

   _____

   _____

2. "When she taught her students, Sahomi explained the story and meaning behind each dance."

   Inference: _____

   _____

   _____

Apply Read the description of each character below. Then write a short paragraph inferring how the character feels without actually stating it.

3. a dog who wants to play

_____

_____

_____

_____

4. a performer who is nervous

_____

_____

_____

_____

5. a boy excited to see his favorite movie

_____

_____

_____

_____

Name _____ Date _____

Making Conjectures

Our question or problem:

_____

_____

_____

_____

Conjecture (my first theory or explanation):

_____

_____

_____

_____

_____

_____

_____

_____

As you collect information, your conjecture will change. Return to this page to record your new theories or explanations about your question or problem.

Establishing Investigation Needs

My group's question or problem:

_____

_____

_____

_____

_____

Knowledge Needs—Information I need to find or figure out in order to investigate the question or problem:

A: _____

B: _____

C: _____

D: _____

E: _____

Source	Useful?	How?
Encyclopedias		
Books		
Magazines		
Newspapers		
Video and Audio Clips		
Television		
Interviews or observations		
Museums		
Other:		

Name _____ Date _____

Writing a Summary: Two Texts

Audience: Who will read your summary?

_____

Purpose: What is your reason for writing a summary?

_____

_____

Prewriting When summarizing more than one text, you need to show similarities and differences. Comparing details shows what the texts have in common. Contrasting details shows how they are different. Use the organizer to compare and contrast "Our Song" with "The Dancing Bird of Paradise."

Subject 1 Our Song	Similarities	Subject 2 The Dancing Bird of Paradise

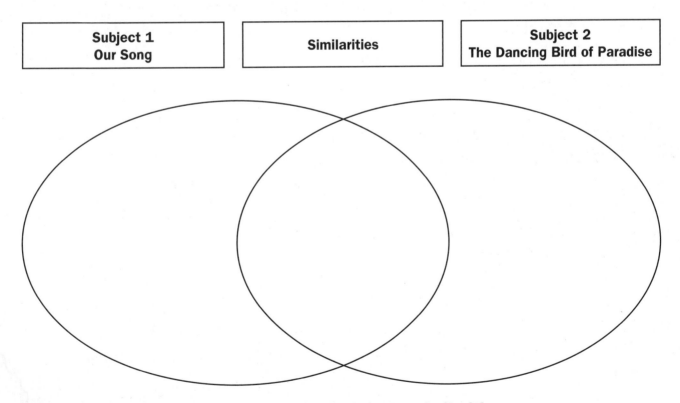

Write two to three paragraphs summarizing the similarities and differences between the two stories.

Revising

Use this checklist to revise your summary.

- ☐ Does your summary have a main idea?
- ☐ Do the details support your main idea?
- ☐ Did you present your comparisons and contrasts in a logical order?
- ☐ Do your comparisons and contrasts make sense?
- ☐ Have you included adjectives and adverbs to make your writing more interesting?

Editing/Proofreading

Use this checklist to correct mistakes.

- ☐ Are your adjectives and adverbs, including comparatives and superlatives, used correctly?
- ☐ Have you checked for errors in spelling, capitalization, and punctuation?
- ☐ Have you read your summary several times to check for mistakes?

Publishing

Use this checklist to share your summary.

- ☐ Neatly type or rewrite your summary.
- ☐ Share your summary with someone who might like either of the stories.

Name _____ Date _____

Spelling

A prefix changes the meaning of the base word it precedes. Identifying prefixes and understanding their meanings can help you figure out the meaning and spelling of a difficult or unfamiliar word. Many words feature the prefixes *un-* and *en-*. The prefix **un-** means "not," or "the opposite of." The prefix **en-** has several meanings: "to put in or into"; "to cause to be"; "thoroughly." These prefixes do not change the spelling of the base words.

Word List

1. enrich
2. unpleasant
3. endanger
4. enable
5. uninspired
6. unlikely
7. encompass
8. unmarked
9. enlarge
10. ungrateful
11. encode
12. enlighten
13. unlimited
14. unsatisfied
15. unsweetened
16. enjoy
17. encourage
18. uneaten
19. enrage
20. unnamed

 **Practice**   Add the prefix *un-* or *en-* to the following base words and write the resulting spelling words on the lines.

1. _____named   _____

2. _____eaten   _____

3. _____joy   _____

4. _____satisfied   _____

5. _____lighten   _____

6. _____grateful   _____

7. _____rich   _____

8. _____danger   _____

9. _____inspired   _____

10. _____compass   _____

11. _____large   _____

12. _____code   _____

13. _____limited   _____

14. _____sweetened   _____

15. _____courage   _____

16. _____rage   _____

17. _____likely   _____

18. _____marked   _____

19. _____able   _____

20. _____pleasant   _____

Apply

The following words are misspelled. Write the correctly spelled spelling word on the line. If the word is already correct, write correct.

21. ennamed   _____

22. ungrateful   _____

23. enmarked   _____

24. unrage   _____

25. enlarge   _____

26. unjoy   _____

27. uncompass   _____

28. ensatisfied   _____

29. enlighten   _____

30. unrich   _____

Name _____   Date _____

Adjectives and Adverbs

Adjectives modify nouns.

- Adjectives show what kind, how many, and which one.
- Proper adjectives, like proper nouns, are always capitalized.

- **colorful** shirts; **several** children
- **French** toast; **Jewish** deli

Adverbs modify verbs, adjectives, and other adverbs.

- Adverbs show how, when, where, and to what extent.

- walked **slowly**; bowled **yesterday**; jumping **around**; **very** quiet

Circle the adjectives, and underline the adverbs in the following paragraph.

Each spring, Washington, D.C. is filled with the colorful

blossoms of Japanese cherry trees. In 1912, Tokyo's mayor

generously donated three thousand trees. They clearly

symbolized the growing friendship between Japan and

America. A two-week festival is held annually to celebrate the

blossoming trees and Japanese culture.

Lesson 3

Apply Read each numbered sentence. On the first line, write *adjective* or *adverb*. On the second line, write the word or phrase from the box that describes how the adjective or adverb functions in the sentence.

how	what kind	where	to what extent
when	how many	which one	

1. Tom, Shane, and Wylie were **deeply** involved in a **card** game.

   a. *Deeply* is an _____; it tells _____.

   b. *Card* is an _____; it tells _____.

2. They **always** relaxed in Shane's **tree** house when it was **too** hot to play basketball.

   a. *Always* is an _____; it tells _____.

   b. *Tree* is an _____; it tells _____.

   c. *Too* is an _____; it tells _____.

3. **Suddenly,** a **loud** crash echoed through Shane's **normally** calm backyard.

   a. *Suddenly* is an _____; it tells _____.

   b. *Loud* is an _____; it tells _____.

   c. *Normally* is an _____; it tells _____.

4. The **two** boys **carefully** climbed **down** from the tree house.

   a. *Two* is an _____; it tells _____.

   b. *Carefully* is an _____; it tells _____.

   c. *Down* is an _____; it tells _____.

Name _____ Date _____

Suffixes -ant, -y, and -ity

Focus

The suffix **-ant** means "being in a particular state" or "one who does something." For example, adding the suffix -ant to the word *serve* changes it to *servant*, or "one who serves."

The suffix **-y** means "having the quality of, state." For example, someone who has *luck* is *lucky*.

The suffix **-ity** means, "the quality or condition of." The suffix converts certain adjectives into nouns. For example, something that is *necessary* is a *necessity*.

Practice Complete each sentence below with a word that uses the suffix *-ant*.

1. Someone who assists is an _____.

2. Someone who immigrates is an _____.

3. Someone who occupies a room is an _____.

4. Someone who inhabits a place is an _____.

5. Someone who sells merchandise is a _____.

Complete each sentence below with a word that uses the suffix -y or -ity.

6. Something that has the quality of being fun is _____.

7. Something that is real represents _____.

8. Something that is considered abnormal is an _____.

9. When the sun is shining outside it is _____.

10. Someone who is civil has _____.

Apply Read the following root words and their definitions. Use each root to create a word that ends with the suffix in parentheses, and then use the new word in a sentence. Use a dictionary if you need help.

11. vac = empty (-ant)

_____

_____

12. gust = sudden burst (-y)

_____

_____

13. dorm = sleep (-ant)

_____

_____

14. bulk = large in size (-y)

_____

_____

15. defy = challenge (-ant)

_____

_____

16. able = having skill to accomplish a task (-ity)

_____

_____

Name _____ Date _____

Selection Vocabulary

Focus

attitude (at' • ə • tōōd') *n.* a way of acting, thinking, or feeling (page 85)

claim (klām) *v.* to declare as one's own (page 85)

magnificent (mag • ni' • fə • sənt) *adj.* outstanding; excellent (page 85)

spellbound (spel' • bound) *adj.* fascinated; filled with delight or wonder (page 86)

civilizations (si' • və • lə • zā' • shənz) *n.* plural of **civilization**: an advanced human society in which agriculture, trade, government, art, and science are highly developed (page 86)

section (sek' • shən) *n.* a part of an area (page 87)

concert (kon' • sûrt') *n.* a musical performance (page 87)

finest (fī' • nəst) *adj.* best; most excellent (page 88)

forbidden (fər • bi' • dən) *adj.* off-limits (page 88)

trolley (trol' • ē) *n.* a streetcar that runs on tracks and gets its power from an electric wire overhead (page 90)

Practice   Write the word from the Focus box that best fits each clue.

1. It is one part of a building, a city, or any other area.

What is it? _____

2. The Egyptians and the Mayans had famous ones.

What are they? _____

3. It is the best ice cream you have ever eaten.

Which word compares it to other ice creams? _____

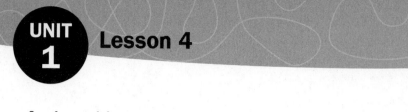

4. A positive one is always better than a negative one.

What is it? _____

5. This musical event can take place in an auditorium or a stadium.

What is it? _____

6. During the most dramatic part of a movie, your mouth hangs open, and you do not want to blink.

What are you? _____

7. Clang! Clang! Clang! Next stop, Telegraph Hill!

Where might you hear this? _____

8. Do not enter! Stop! You are not allowed inside!

What kind of place would have these messages? _____

9. A lost glove waits quietly in a Lost and Found box.

What does it need someone to do to it? _____

10. Critics love it! Audiences agree. It is an excellent film.

What word describes this movie? _____

Apply **Select the word that completes each sentence.**

11. The auditorium was filled with _____ decorations.

12. The front _____ of our yard has been dug up.

13. Keiko was _____ as she watched the magician.

14. To succeed in life, it is helpful to have a good _____.

15. Mr. Pérez's bakery makes the _____ bread in town.

16. You cannot _____ that book because the library owns it.

Name _____ Date _____

Describing an Object

Think | **Audience: Who** will read your description?

_____

Purpose: What do you want your description to do?

_____

Prewriting | Close your eyes and visualize the object you want to describe. This method will help you focus on the most important details. Use the following graphic organizer to plan your description.

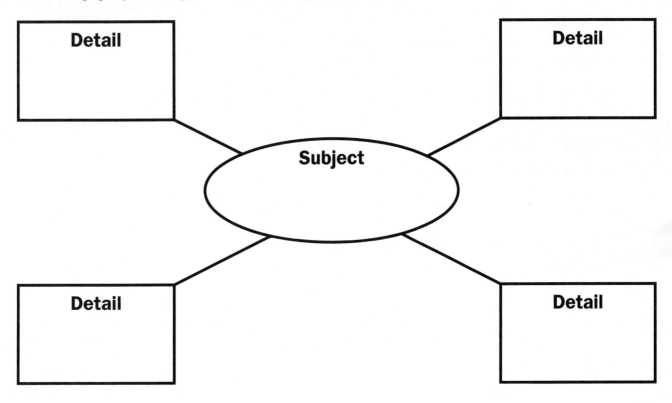

Revising — Use this checklist to revise your description.

- ☐ Are your details grouped in a way that makes sense?
- ☐ Have you chosen vivid and descriptive words so your reader can identify your object?
- ☐ Have you used sensory language or figurative language, such as similes and metaphors?

Editing/Proofreading — Use this checklist to edit your description.

- ☐ Did you use commas and other punctuation correctly?
- ☐ Have you checked your description for capitalization or spelling errors?
- ☐ Have you read through your description several times to check for mistakes?
- ☐ Start making a list of the errors you are commonly making.

Publishing — Use this checklist to publish your description.

- ☐ Neatly rewrite your final copy in cursive handwriting.
- ☐ Post your description and illustration in the classroom.

Name _____ Date _____

Spelling

Focus

- Understanding and identifying suffixes and their meanings can help you determine the meaning and spelling of a difficult or unfamiliar word. Many words feature the suffixes -y, -ity, and -ant.

- The suffix **-y** means "having the quality of, state or condition."

- The suffix **-ity** means "state or quality of."

- The suffix **-ant** means "one who" when added to a verb to make a noun. It means "being in a particular state" or "one that does a particular action or promotes a particular state" when added to a word to make it an adjective.

Word List

1. modesty
2. vigilant
3. servant
4. necessity
5. civility
6. honesty
7. nobility
8. assistant
9. immigrant
10. lucky
11. messy
12. agility
13. rainy
14. pleasant
15. hostility
16. defiant
17. tasty
18. resistant
19. purity
20. formality

Practice

Write the spelling word that results when the suffix -ity, -ant, or -y is added to the following base words or word parts.

1. formal _____

2. necess _____

3. agile _____

4. noble _____

5. hostile _____

6. civil _____

7. pure _____

8. resist _____

9. vigil _____

10. please _____

11. assist _____

12. serve _____

13. immigrate _____

14. defy _____

15. taste _____

16. rain _____

17. modest _____

18. luck _____

19. honest _____

20. mess _____

Apply

Correct the misspelled words and write them on the line. If the word is already correct, write correct.

21. servent _____

22. honestty _____

23. nobilty _____

24. assistant _____

25. pureity _____

26. formalty _____

27. modestity _____

28. messy _____

Name _____ Date _____

Commas

> **Focus**
>
> **Commas** are used to organize the thoughts and items in a sentence. They show the reader where to pause so that a sentence's meaning can be clearly understood.
>
> - Use a comma to separate three or more items.
> - Use a comma after long introductory phrases or dependent clauses.
> - Use a comma and a conjunction to join two independent clauses.
> - Use a comma when an interjection is not followed by an exclamation point.
> - Use a comma before and after an appositive.
>
> - I eat bananas**,** apples**,** and oranges.
> - **After we finished cleaning the house,** my dad and I relaxed.
> - Luiz wants to play chess**, but** Shonda wants to play checkers.
> - **Gosh,** I did not know that. **Hi,** Mr. Harris.
> - My friend**, Lacy,** is going to Kentucky.

Practice

The commas are missing or used incorrectly in the following sentences. On a separate sheet of paper, rewrite each sentence so that it is correct.

1. During our trip, to Texas we will drive through Tennessee, and Arkansas.

2. Hildy put on, a coat a hat a scarf and mittens and, then she went outside.

3. Well that is a great story but, I am not sure I believe it.

4. After five years, in college John my cousin is, about to graduate.

5. We washed dried and peeled, the potatoes, before cutting them into small pieces.

Apply **Insert commas where they are needed in the following paragraph.**

W. E. B. DuBois an important American civil rights leader was also a writer poet editor and historian. DuBois graduated from Harvard University in 1890 and then he studied in Europe for a few years. After returning to the United States DuBois became the first black man to earn a Ph.D. from Harvard. DuBois' most famous book *The Souls of Black Folk* was published in 1903. He was also a founding member of the NAACP or the National Association for the Advancement of Colored People. When DuBois died in 1963 he was a citizen of Ghana a country in Africa.

Name _____ Date _____

Suffixes *-ence* and *-ly* and the Inflectional Ending *-ing*

Focus

- The suffix **-ence** means "state or quality of being." For example, *innocence* means "the quality of being innocent."

- When **-ing** is added to a verb, it forms the present participle. It can be used as a verb, adjective, or noun.

  I saw my friend **running** down the street. (participle)

  Running is good exercise. (noun)

  I bought a pair of **running** shoes. (adjective)

- The suffix **–ly** means "like or resembling." When added to a root or base word the suffix forms adjectives, as in *lovely,* or adverbs, as in *beautifully.*

Practice

Each sentence below contains a boldfaced word with one of the suffixes covered in this lesson. On the line, write *P* if the word is an adverb, *N* if it is a noun, or *A* if it is an adjective.

1. _____ Maurice uses a **shopping** cart when he goes to the store.

2. _____ I **slowly** licked the ice cream melting down the side of the cone.

3. _____ Sometimes Mr. Harrera uses a **sliding** scale to grade papers.

4. _____ The Fourth of July is a celebration of America's **independence.**

5. _____ You could still see the **dissolving** salt in the liquid.

6. _____ Before the trial, the defendant proclaimed his **innocence.**

Apply   Complete the "word-math" problems below. Then use each solution in a sentence.

7. evident + ence = _____

_____

_____

8. unusual + ly = _____

_____

_____

9. nurse + ing = _____

_____

_____

10. selfish + ly = _____

_____

_____

11. comical + ly = _____

_____

_____

12. sail + ing = _____

_____

_____

Name _____ Date _____

Selection Vocabulary

Focus

vast (vast) *adj.* great in size (page 101)

tilted (tilt' • əd) *v.* past tense of **tilt:** to raise one side of (page 101)

withered (with' • ərd) *v.* past tense of **wither:** to dry up from a loss of moisture (page 101)

inhabit (in • ha' • bət) *v.* to live in or on (page 103)

role (rōl) *n.* a position or function (page 109)

luxury (lug' • shoo • rē) *adj.* expensive (page 109)

freighter (frā' • tər) *n.* a ship used for carrying cargo (page 110)

sewage (soo' • ij) *n.* waste that is carried off in sewers and drains (page 111)

lagoon (lə • goon') *n.* a shallow body of water usually connected to a larger body of water (page 111)

fluent (floo' • ənt) *adj.* able to speak effortlessly (page 113)

Practice Write *T* in the blank if the sentence for the vocabulary word is correct. Write *F* if the sentence is false. For every *F* answer, write the word that fits the definition.

1. A freighter is a ship for carrying cargo. ___ _____

2. A luxury car would be expensive.

   ___ _____

3. To inhabit means "to live in or on something."

   ___ _____

4. A lagoon is a function or a position. ___ _____

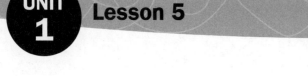

5. Sewage is waste that is carried off in sewers or drains.

___ _____

6. Fluent means "very great in size or number." ___ _____

7. Withered means "raised one side of." ___ _____

8. A lagoon is a shallow body of water connected to a larger one.

___ _____

9. One who is vast in a language can speak it effortlessly.

___ _____

10. Withered leaves are dried up from a loss of moisture.

___ _____

 Apply **Circle the correct letter to answer each question below.**

11. Which is an example of a *role?*
   a. the principal
   b. the filing cabinet

12. Which is an example of something that is *tilted?*
   a. a table with books on it
   b. a table on which balls always roll off one side

13. Which is an example of *inhabit?*
   a. the birds living in the tree
   b. the birds catching insects as they fly

14. Which is an example of something you would find in a *lagoon?*
   a. a rowboat
   b. a car

Name _____ Date _____

Compare and Contrast

Focus Writers compare and contrast to paint a clearer picture of the people and things they are writing about.

- To **compare** means to tell how things, ideas, events, or characters are alike.
- To **contrast** means to tell how things, ideas, events, or characters are different.

Practice **Look through "In Two Worlds: A Yup'ik Eskimo Family," and contrast the Scammon Bay of Mary Ann's childhood and the Scammon Bay of today.**

1. In Mary Ann's time: _____

_____

_____

Today: _____

_____

_____

2. In Mary Ann's time: _____

_____

_____

Today: _____

_____

_____

Apply **Read each sentence, and determine whether it shows a comparison or a contrast. Then, rewrite each sentence reflecting the other term.**

3. Dave and Ed both finished all their vegetables. _____

_____

4. Martha plays the trombone, while Janet plays the cello. _____

_____

5. I like to read mysteries just like my sister Gina. _____

_____

6. Both cats and dogs make good pets. _____

_____

7. Jacob and Jason are twins, but Jacob is slightly taller. _____

_____

On a separate sheet of paper, write a paragraph comparing and contrasting yourself to a friend or relative. Be sure to include ways that you are similar and ways that you are different.

Comprehension Skill • *Skills Practice 1*

Name _____ Date _____

Magazine Articles

Think **Audience: Who** will read your magazine article?

_____

Purpose: What is your reason for writing a magazine article?

_____

Prewriting Magazine articles tell their readers about important events. The information in an article needs to be accurate and complete. Journalists use the following six questions to make sure their stories include all of the facts. Answer the questions to make sure your article will be accurate and complete.

What happened? _____

_____

Where did it happen? _____

_____

Who was involved? _____

_____

When did it happen? _____

_____

Why did it happen? _____

_____

How did it happen? _____

_____

Revising

Use this checklist to revise your draft.

- ☐ Have you varied the introductory phrases in your sentences so that your article does not sound repetitive?
- ☐ Have you varied sentence types to create rhythm and interest?
- ☐ Does your opening paragraph grab the reader's attention with an interesting lead?
- ☐ Have you used descriptive words?

Editing/Proofreading

Use this checklist to look for mistakes in your draft.

- ☐ Have you spelled proper nouns consistently throughout the article?
- ☐ Have you checked the events in your story against the time line that you made?
- ☐ Have you checked your facts more than once?

Publishing

Use this checklist to share your draft.

- ☐ Have a friend or classmate read your draft.
- ☐ Listen carefully to his or her suggestions, and decide which ones you will use.

Name _____ Date _____

Spelling

Focus

Understanding and identifying suffixes and their meanings can help you determine the meaning and spelling of a difficult or unfamiliar word. The suffix **-ly** changes an adjective into an adverb. It means "like or resembling." When the suffix *-ly* changes a noun to an adjective, it means "resembling." It rarely changes the spelling of the base word to which it is added. The suffix **-ence** means "state or quality of," and, when added to a word, makes the word a noun.

Word List

1. independence
2. finally
3. convenience
4. wisely
5. violence
6. timidly
7. absence
8. cautiously
9. turbulence
10. silently
11. emergence
12. desperately
13. excellence
14. accurately
15. difference
16. strictly
17. reference
18. beautifully
19. competence
20. directly

Practice Drop the suffix *-ly* from each word and write the resulting word on the line.

1. finally _____

2. wisely _____

3. timidly _____

4. cautiously _____

5. silently _____

6. desperately _____

7. accurately _____

8. strictly _____

9. beautifully _____

10. directly _____

On the line, write the spelling word that results when the suffix -ence is added to the following base words or word parts.

11. compete _____

12. absent _____

13. convenient _____

14. turbulent _____

15. emerge _____

16. excel _____

17. refer _____

18. independent _____

19. violent _____

20. differ _____

Apply   **Select the correct word from the parentheses that completes each sentence and write it on the line.**

21. The little boy smiled _____ (timid, timidly) at the doctor.

22. She sang the song _____. (beautiful, beautifully)

23. The dog _____ (cautious, cautiously) sniffed the air before going outside.

24. The students read the book _____. (silently, silence)

25. The town sheriff _____ (strict, strictly) enforced the law.

26. They tried _____ (desperate, desperately) to save the man's life.

Name _____ Date _____

Verbs, Verb Phrases, and Objects

Focus

- **Verbs** are words that show action or express a state of being.

- **Verb phrases** consist of one or more helping verbs used with an action or state-of-being verb.

- **Direct objects** are nouns and pronouns that receive the action of the verb.

- **Indirect objects** are nouns and pronouns for or to whom something is done.

- **Objects** are also the nouns and pronouns that appear in prepositional phrases.

- Malcolm **grew** tomatoes and peppers.
  Tomorrow **is** the last day of school.

- I **have picked** a book for my report.
  She **could see** the deer running.

- Pilar finished her **homework.**
  The artist sculpted a **statue.**

- Denzel told his **classmates** a joke.
  We made our **mother** dinner.

- Take me to the **mall.**
  The bird flew over my **head.**

Practice

In the following sentences, circle the verb or verb phrase, and underline the direct object(s) once and the indirect object(s) twice.

1. Natalie waited inside the cab.

2. Sometimes our garbage smells like rotten eggs.

3. Next year I will read Tom Sawyer.

4. The astronauts could see Earth from outer space.

5. The pitcher threw the batter a curve ball.

6. The concert was held near an old, abandoned factory.

7. Soon my order will arrive by special delivery.

8. Omar drew his friend a picture of some horses.

Apply The verb or verb phrase in each sentence below has been boldfaced. On the first line, write *A* if it is an action verb or *S* if it is a state-of-being verb. One object in each sentence has also been boldfaced. On the second line, write *D* if it is a direct object, *I* if it is an indirect object, or *P* if it is the object of the preposition.

9. Verb: _____   Object: _____
The bus **carries students** to and from school every day.

10. Verb: _____   Object: _____
I **have been** sick with the **flu** for almost a week.

11. Verb: _____   Object: _____
Lina **sold** Enrique her old **watch.**

12. Verb: _____   Object: _____
The violinist **seemed** satisfied with her **performance.**

13. Verb: _____   Object: _____
Mr. Lin **has told Maxwell** a story about his childhood.

14. Verb: _____   Object: _____
John **understood** the **rules** before he began playing the game.

Name _____ Date _____

Compound Words and the Prefix *in-*

Focus

- **Compound words** are words formed by combining two or more smaller words into one larger word. If you know the smaller words' meanings, you can often figure out the meaning of the compound. For example, a *backpack* is a pack you carry on your back.

- The prefix **in-** means "not," "lacking," or "lack of." Adding *in-* to a base word usually creates a word with the opposite meaning. For example, *incorrect* means "not correct," or the opposite of *correct.*

Practice

On the lines below, write definitions for each pair of words. Then write a definition for the compound word they form. Use a dictionary if you need help.

1. saw: _____

    dust: _____

    sawdust: _____

2. head: _____

    ache: _____

    headache: _____

3. hand: _____

    made: _____

    handmade: _____

Add the prefix *in-* to the following words and use a dictionary to define each word.

4. difference _____

5. direct _____

6. dependent _____

Apply **Add the prefix *in-* to each word below, and then use the new word in a sentence. Include the compound word listed in your sentence.**

7. _____complete — sandcastle

_____

_____

8. _____direct — landmarks

_____

_____

9. _____convenient — homework

_____

_____

10. _____active — underground

_____

_____

Name _____ Date _____

Selection Vocabulary

Focus

dissolve (di • zolv')
v. to mix into liquid
(page 138)

retirement (ri • tīr' • mənt) *n.* the
act of taking oneself away from
a job or occupation (page 139)

inefficient (in' • ə • fish' • ənt)
adj. not offering a good use of
money or effort (page 139)

vents (vents) *n.* plural of **vent:**
an opening through which a gas
passes (page 139)

charged (chärjd) *v.* past tense
of **charge:** to fill with electricity
(page 141)

demonstration (de' • mən •
strā' • shən) *n.* something that
explains, proves, or shows
something clearly (page 141)

donors (dō' • nərz) *n.* plural
of **donor:** a person who gives
something (page 142)

electrocuted (i • lek' • trə •
kyōōt' • əd) *v.* past tense of
electrocute: to kill by means
of a very strong electric shock
(page 143)

attracted (ə • trak' • təd) *v.* past
tense of **attract:** to cause to
come near (page 144)

insulators (in' • sə • lā' • tərz)
n. plural of **insulator:** a material
that does not carry an electric
charge (page 144)

Practice **Fill in each blank with the vocabulary word
that best completes the sentence.**

1. Mr. Flores gave a _____ of how to perform CPR.

2. Delivering one pizza at a time would be an _____
way to work.

3. With help from several _____, the Debate Club
purchased a new podium.

4. My grandma's _____ has given her more time for volunteering.

5. That new bird seed _____ nearly a dozen yellow finches to our backyard.

6. _____ the salt in the water before you add the yeast.

7. DeShawn _____ his cell phone's battery before leaving for work.

8. Dryer _____ carry warm, damp air outdoors.

9. The _____ covering the wires were necessary to protect the workers working on the electric line from being

_____ .

Apply
Write the vocabulary word that matches each definition below.

10. _____ openings through which gases pass

11. _____ something that explains a process

12. _____ materials that do not carry electrical charges

13. _____ caused to come near

14. _____ people who give

15. _____ to mix into liquid

16. _____ filled with electricity

17. _____ killed by a strong electric shock

18. _____ not offering a good use of money or effort

Name _____ Date _____

Recording Concept Information

As I read the selection, this is what I added to my understanding of energy at work.

- "The Sparks Fly" by Ruth Ashby

  _____

  _____

  _____

- "Tailing Tornadoes" by Trudi Strain Trueit

  _____

  _____

  _____

- "Jake Drake Know-It-All" by Andrew Clements

  _____

  _____

  _____

- "The Wind at Work" by Gretchen Woelfle

  _____

  _____

  _____

- "What are Food Chains and Webs?" by Bobbie Kalman

  _____

  _____

  _____

UNIT 2 Lesson 1

Knowledge about Energy at Work

- This is what I know about energy at work before reading the unit.

_____

_____

_____

_____

_____

- These are some things about energy at work that I would like to talk about and understand better.

_____

_____

_____

_____

_____

Reminder: I should read this page again when I get to the end of the unit to see how much my ideas about energy at work have changed.

Name _____ **Date** _____

Ideas about Energy at Work

Of the ideas discussed in class about energy at work, these are the ones I found most interesting.

_____

_____

_____

_____

_____

_____

_____

_____

_____

_____

_____

_____

_____

_____

_____

_____

_____

Ideas about Energy at Work (continued)

Write down the ideas you found most interesting about the selection "The Sparks Fly." Discuss your ideas with the class.

_____

_____

_____

_____

_____

_____

_____

_____

_____

_____

_____

_____

_____

_____

_____

_____

_____

_____

Name _____ Date _____

Science Observation Report

Think   **Audience: Who** will read the report of your experiment?

_____

Purpose: What is your reason for conducting an experiment?

_____

_____

Prewriting   **It is important to follow the steps of the scientific process. Use the lines below to begin your experiment.**

Problem: _____

Hypothesis: _____

Procedure: _____

_____

_____

_____

_____

_____

    The final step in your experiment is to draw conclusions based on your observations. Do your observations support your hypothesis? Write a paragraph summarizing your conclusions.

Revising
Use this checklist to revise the report of your experiment.

☐ Have you referred to data and included your observations?

☐ Have you included all of your observations?

☐ Have you presented the steps of the scientific process in their proper order?

☐ Did you use transition words to show the sequence of events?

☐ Have you varied your sentence type and length so your report is interesting to read?

Editing/Proofreading
Use this checklist to correct mistakes.

☐ Have you labeled the steps of the scientific process correctly?

☐ Did you check all capitalization, punctuation, and spelling?

☐ Have you read your report more than once to check for correctly applied rules for regular and irregular plurals?

Publishing
Use this checklist to publish your results.

☐ Rewrite your report neatly, or type it on a computer.

☐ The final step in the scientific process is to share the results of your experiment with others. For example, you could read your report to the class.

Name _____ Date _____

Spelling

Focus
• **Compound words** consist of two smaller words that have been combined to form one larger word. These two words keep the same spelling in the compound word.

• The prefix **in-** has several meanings. It means "not"; or it can mean "within," "into," or "on."

Practice
Combine the two smaller words to make a compound word from the word list and write it on the line.

1. news + break = _____

2. double + header = _____

3. head + quarters = _____

4. key + board = _____

5. wind + shield = _____

Add the prefix in- to the following base words to form words from the spelling list and write them on the lines.

6. finite _____

7. accurate _____

8. experienced _____

9. efficient _____

10. justice _____

Word List
1. indefinite
2. doubleheader
3. eyewitness
4. inefficient
5. inaccurate
6. windshield
7. loudspeaker
8. undertake
9. headquarters
10. inexperienced
11. keyboard
12. infinite
13. inability
14. injustice
15. grasshopper
16. overindulge
17. insight
18. involuntary
19. newsbreak
20. inconsiderate

Apply On the line, write the spelling word from the list that best fits each definition.

21. a breaking news story _____

22. a board with keys on it _____

23. a witness who sees something firsthand _____

24. an insect that hops over the grass _____

25. to indulge too much _____

26. a double set of games played one after the other _____

27. a speaker that makes your voice loud and easily heard _____

28. the place where the head part of a company has its quarters _____

29. part of a car that shields you from the wind _____

30. to take on something, such as a new project _____

Use the following phrases and select the spelling word that fits the description best. Write the word on the line.

31. not experienced _____

32. not efficient _____

33. not voluntary _____

34. without ability _____

35. the opposite of justice _____

36. not considerate _____

37. seeing into _____

38. not definite _____

39. not accurate _____

40. not ending _____

Name _____ Date _____

Action Verbs

Focus

- **Action verbs** add energy and precision to sentences. The action of the verbs can express mental or physical action.

- Action verbs can be the main verbs in verb phrases.

- Action verbs can also be found in dependent clauses.

- I **understand** what you are saying.

- Ted has been **thinking** it over.

- I was relieved when Jen **asked** for help. It was cold because someone **opened** a door.

Practice **Circle the action verbs in the paragraph below.**

Last week, our class visited the Science Museum. We saw several demonstrations that used electricity. My friend Lana was a volunteer in one of them. Her long hair stood up on end when a wand was waved over her head. Later, she told me that she knew what would happen because she had been to the museum before. I hope that next time I can volunteer for that experiment!

Apply Write a sentence that contains an action verb for each noun listed below. Then, underline the action verbs in your sentences.

1. trees

_____

_____

2. baseball

_____

_____

3. bus driver

_____

_____

4. light bulb

_____

_____

5. magazine

_____

_____

6. freeway

_____

_____

Name _____ Date _____

Word Origins

> **Focus** Recognizing and understanding **word origins** can help you understand new and unfamiliar words. For example, take the word *microscopic.* It contains the Greek root *scop.* This root means "to look at." The prefix *micro-* means "very small." Thus *microscopic* means "too small to be seen."

> **Practice** The following words originate from the same language. They each contain a Latin root that has been defined for you. On the line, write a different word that uses the same root.

1. liberate

   Latin root *liber* means, "to free": _____

2. portable

   Latin root *port* means "carry": _____

3. reform

   Latin root *form* means "shape": _____

4. prediction

   Latin root *dic* means, "speak": _____

5. abrupt

   Latin root *rupt* means, "to break": _____

Apply The words below are Greek in origin. The meanings of their roots, prefixes, and suffixes have been provided for you. Define each word based on the meanings of its parts. Check your answers in a dictionary.

6. the prefix *pro-* = in front of

Greek root *logue* = word

prologue = _____

7. the prefix *dia-* = across or through

Greek root *meter* = measure

diameter = _____

8. Greek root *path* = disease or illness

the suffix *-ology* = study or science of

pathology = _____

9. the prefix *syn-* = together

Greek root *chron* = time

the suffix *-ize* = to make

synchronize = _____

10. Greek root *aero* = air

the suffix *-ate* = to make

aerate = _____

Name _____   Date _____

Selection Vocabulary

Focus

layer (lā' • ər) *n.* one thickness of something (page 154)

raging (rā' • jing) *adj.* very active and unpredictable (page 155)

survey (sûr' • vā) *n.* an inspection or investigation (page 155)

opposing (ə • pōz' • ing) *adj.* opposite; completely different (page 156)

prediction (pri • dik' • shən) *n.* the act of telling something before it happens (page 156)

severe (sə • vir') *adj.* very serious; dangerous (page 157)

stovepipe (stōv' • pīp') *n.* a thin pipe connected to a stove that directs smoke or fumes out of an area (page 160)

spiraling (spī' • rəl • ing) *v.* moving in the shape of a spiral (page 160)

inspiration (in' • spə • rā' • shən) *n.* the stirring of the mind, feelings, or imagination, especially so that some good idea comes (page 160)

alert (ə • lûrt') *adj.* awake and prepared to act (page 161)

Practice **Write the vocabulary word next to the group of words that have a similar meaning.**

1. encouragement; stirring; prompting _____

2. differing; conflicting; contradictory _____

3. serious; critical; risky _____

4. aware; watchful; attentive _____

5. wild; unpredictable; turbulent _____

6. forecast; projection; speculation _____

7. piece; slab; level; _____

8. winding; twisting; turning _____

9. investigation; study; research _____

10. chimney; smokestack _____

Apply **Draw a line to match each word on the left to its definition on the right.**

11. prediction

12. survey

13. inspiration

14. layer

15. severe

16. stovepipe

17. alert

18. raging

19. spiraling

20. opposing

a. awake and prepared to act

b. one thickness of something

c. the act of telling something before it happens

d. very active and unpredictable

e. the stirring of the feelings or imagination

f. opposite; completely different

g. an inspection or investigation

h. moving in the shape of a spiral

i. a thin pipe connected to a stove that directs smoke out of an area

j. very serious; dangerous

Name _____ **Date** _____

Formulating Questions and Problems

A good question or problem to investigate:

_____

_____

_____

_____

_____

Why this is an interesting question or problem:

_____

_____

_____

_____

_____

Some other things I wonder about this question or problem:

_____

_____

_____

_____

_____

Formulating Questions and Problems (continued)

My investigation group's question or problem:

_____

_____

_____

_____

_____

What our investigation will contribute to the rest of the class:

_____

_____

_____

_____

_____

Some other things I wonder about this question or problem:

_____

_____

_____

_____

_____

Name _____ **Date** _____

Gardener's Almanac

Think

Audience: Who will read your article?

_____

Purpose: What is your reason for writing a gardening article?

_____

_____

Prewriting

When you use someone else's knowledge or ideas, you must give that person credit. Find some information about lima beans in each type of source listed below. Write the information you find in your Learning Log, and then use the lines below to begin writing a bibliography. Be sure to use the correct format for each type of source.

Book: _____

_____

_____

Encyclopedia: _____

_____

_____

Internet site: _____

_____

_____

_____

Revising

Use this checklist to revise the report of your experiment.

☐ Is your hypothesis clearly stated?

☐ Do your observations and research support the advice you provide?

☐ Have you included enough information from your Learning Log notes and clearly organized them?

☐ Have you cited all your sources in a bibliography?

Editing/Proofreading

Use this checklist to correct mistakes.

☐ Have you used the proper format for each type of source in your bibliography?

☐ Did you check all capitalization, punctuation, and spelling?

☐ Have you read your report more than once to check for correctly used conjunctions throughout your almanac?

☐ Did you review any suspicious information and double-check your facts?

Publishing

Use this checklist to publish your results.

☐ Rewrite your report neatly, or type it on a computer.

☐ Add graphs, charts, or other helpful illustrations to your report.

☐ Share your report with your teacher or a classmate.

Name _____ Date _____

Spelling

Focus

- The prefix *ir-* means "not".
- The prefix *dis-* has several meanings: "opposite" or "lack of" or "not."
- **Root words** were formed from words of other languages, such as Greek and Latin. Here are some roots in the spelling words and their meanings:

  port = carry; *sign* = mark

Practice Write the spelling word which is formed by adding the prefix *ir-* or *dis-* to each of the word parts.

1. ir + reparable = _____

2. ir + refutable = _____

3. dis + appearing = _____

4. dis + interest = _____

Fill in the root word and write the resulting spelling word on the line.

sign

5. _____ature   _____

6. _____ify   _____

port

7. _____able   _____

8. _____er   _____

Word List

1. discouraged
2. irregular
3. portable
4. import
5. displace
6. irrelevant
7. sign
8. signify
9. disembark
10. signal
11. exporting
12. disappearing
13. irrefutable
14. porter
15. transportation
16. disinterest
17. signature
18. insignia
19. irrational
20. irreparable

Apply

Fill in the blanks with the appropriate letters to create a spelling word from the list and write it on the line.

9. p_____able = _____

10. _____regular = _____

11. _____embark = _____

12. s_____al = _____

13. _____relevant = _____

14. in_____ia = _____

15. _____appearing = _____

16. p_____er = _____

17. trans_____ation = _____

18. s_____n = _____

19. ex_____ing = _____

20. im_____ = _____

21. _____couraged = _____

22. _____refutable = _____

23. _____ature = _____

24. _____reparable = _____

25. _____ify = _____

26. _____place = _____

27. _____interest = _____

28. _____rational = _____

Name _____ Date _____

Electronic Technology: Retrieving and Reviewing Information

Focus

- Searching for and retrieving information is much easier because of **electronic technology.** The Internet, online encyclopedias, and electronic library catalogs provide quick access to large amounts of information. Knowing how to choose **keywords** for your searches is an important skill in using electronic technology.

- Electronic technology also helps you review the things you have written. **Word-processing programs** can check for errors in spelling and grammar. They will not catch every error, however; you must still proofread your work. For example, homophones and homographs are often overlooked by word-processing programs.

Practice A word-processing program corrected most of the errors in the paragraph below. However, there are four errors it did not catch. Read the paragraph carefully, and circle the errors.

Thomas Edison was borne in 1847 in Milan, Ohio. During his teen years, Edison worked several odd jobs before becoming a telegraph operator. His fist inventions used telegraph technology to send information like stock numbers and vote tallies. Edison became a household name with his invention off the phonograph in 1877. People were amazed to here voices coming from a machine.

Explain why the word-processing program may have missed these errors.

_____

_____

_____

Apply Read the research topics below. Write at least two keywords you would use to begin a search for information about each topic.

1. How do birds know when to migrate?

_____

2. What are the words in Abraham Lincoln's Gettysburg Address?

_____

3. How does milk get from a cow to your refrigerator?

_____

4. Where is the tallest tree in the world located?

_____

5. Who wrote _The Decline and Fall of the Roman Empire?_

_____

6. Who is the current president of Angola?

_____

7. Which ocean is the largest?

_____

8. What is the function of your kidneys?

_____

Name _____ Date _____

Inflectional Ending -ed

Focus

- Adding the **inflectional ending -ed** to a verb creates the past tense of the verb.

  They **work** from dawn to dusk.
  They **worked** from dawn to dusk.

- Verbs that end with the inflectional ending -ed can also form the past participle. This verb form can be used as a verb or an adjective.

  That **baked** apple smells great!

Practice Rewrite the following sentences so that they are in the past tense.

1. The astronauts land their spaceship on another planet.

   _____

2. My friends and I dine in the cafeteria.

   _____

3. The horses carry the riders along the trail.

   _____

4. The workers rip long strips of wallpaper off the wall.

   _____

5. I type my research paper on the computer.

   _____

6. My calves itch where they touched poison ivy.

   _____

Apply

A word ending in -ed has been boldfaced in each sentence below. On the line, write V if the word is used as a verb, or A if it is an adjective.

7. _____ A motorcycle **zipped** past us on the freeway.

8. _____ For dessert, Ms. Christo usually eats **canned** peaches sprinkled with sugar.

9. _____ Amy's **knotted** hair took half an hour to untangle.

10. _____ I **switched** places with Jasmine in social studies.

11. _____ I looked closely at the **graded** tests.

12. _____ Luiz and his uncle drank **iced** tea on the porch.

13. _____ The nurse **checked** on the patients in his care.

14. _____ We **shredded** cheese to spread on the pizza.

Name _____ **Date** _____

Selection Vocabulary

Focus

electromagnets (i • lek' • trō • mag' • nits) *n.* plural of **electromagnet:** a piece of iron with wire wound around it. It becomes a magnet when an electric current is passed through the wire. (page 170)

squinted (skwint' • əd) *v.* past tense of **squint:** to partially close the eyes (page 173)

observe (əb • zûrv') *v.* to make a careful study of (page 174)

crane (krān) *n.* a large machine with a long arm that can be moved up and down and in a circle. Cables at the end of the crane's arm are used to lift and move heavy objects. (page 174)

hypothesis (hī • poth' • i • sis) *n.* something that is suggested as being true for the purposes of further investigation (page 175)

positive (po' • zi • tiv) *adj.* having one of two opposite kinds of electric charge (page 179)

negative (neg' • ə • tiv) *adj.* having one of two opposite kinds of electric charge (page 179)

practically (prak' • tik • lē) *adv.* nearly; almost (page 181)

conclusions (kən • klo͞o' • zhənz) *n.* plural of **conclusion:** something decided after thinking and experimenting (page 181)

Practice

Write the vocabulary word on the line that best completes each sentence.

1. The scientist's experiments proved that his _____ was correct.

2. Electricity contains both _____ and positive charges.

3. _____ closely how the magician makes the cards disappear.

4. The runner _____ fell after slipping on the wet track.

5. The giant crane uses _____ to lift heavy objects.

6. A negative charge is attracted to a _____ charge.

7. The builders used a _____ to lift steel beams onto the roof.

8. After leaving the dark theater, I _____ because of the bright sunlight.

9. Dr. Wong and Dr. Shepherd drew different _____ from the X-rays.

10. We had _____ finished building the model when my dog sat on it.

Apply Write *C* in the blank if the selection vocabulary word has been defined correctly. Write *I* in the blank if it has been defined incorrectly, and write the correct word on the line.

11. *Positive* means "something that is suggested as being true for the purposes of an investigation."

   _____   _____

12. To *observe* means "to make a careful study of."

   _____   _____

13. *Conclusions* are things decided after thinking and experimenting.

   _____   _____

14. *Cranes* are pieces of iron wrapped in wire with electric currents running through them.

   _____   _____

Name _____ Date _____

Making Conjectures

Our question or problem:

_____

_____

_____

_____

_____

Conjecture (my first theory or explanation):

_____

_____

_____

_____

_____

As you collect information, your conjecture will change. Return to this page to record your new theories or explanations about your question or problem.

Establishing Investigation Needs

My group's question or problem:

_____

_____

_____

_____

Knowledge Needs—Information I need to find or figure out in order to investigate the question or problem:

A. _____

B. _____

C. _____

D. _____

E. _____

Source	Useful?	How?
Encyclopedias		
Books		
Magazines		
Newspapers		
Video and Audio Clips		
Television		
Interviews, observations		
Museums		
Other		

Name _____ **Date** _____

Book Review

Think   Audience: **Who** will read your book review?

_____

Purpose: **What** do you want your book review to do?

_____

_____

Prewriting   **A book review should summarize the plot, describe the characters, and offer an opinion about the book. Use this graphic organizer to help plan your book review.**

Title	
Author's Purpose	
Summary	
Your Opinions	
Your Recommendation	

Revising   Use this checklist to revise your book review.

☐ Did you include an introduction that gives the basic facts about your book, such as title and author?

☐ Have you described the major characters or people who appear in the book?

☐ Does your summary give the reader a clear idea of the plot?

☐ Have you clearly stated your recommendations and opinions about the book?

Editing/Proofreading   Use this checklist to correct mistakes.

☐ Did you spell the title and author's name correctly?

☐ Do your nouns and pronouns agree?

☐ Did you check for spelling errors, including those errors missed by a spell-checker?

Publishing   Use this checklist to prepare for publication.

☐ Rewrite your book review neatly, or type it on a computer.

☐ Share your book review with the class by reading it aloud.

Name _____   Date _____

Spelling

- When you add the **inflectional ending -ed** to a verb, it forms the past tense of that verb. Drop the e if a word ends in e. If a word is more than one syllable and ends in *-er*, do not change the spelling of the base word if the last syllable is not accented. If the word ends in a short vowel followed by a single consonant, then double the consonant.

- The prefix *il-* means "not," and is added to words that begin with *l*.

- **Synonyms** are words with the same, or nearly the same, meaning. A word may have many synonyms that have slightly different meanings.

Word List

1. pictured
2. illiterate
3. laminated
4. registered
5. supposed
6. featured
7. uproar
8. tumult
9. extraordinary
10. pandemonium
11. illegible
12. illegal
13. selected
14. wonderful
15. inflamed
16. illogical
17. marvelous
18. consistent
19. hindered
20. complimented

Practice   Add the prefix *il-* or the inflectional ending *-ed* to the following base words to form spelling words from the list. Write the words on the lines.

1. picture   _____
2. suppose   _____
3. logical   _____
4. legal   _____
5. literate   _____
6. laminate   _____
7. legible   _____
8. feature   _____
9. register   _____

Spelling (cont.)

10. select _____

11. inflame _____

12. hinder _____

13. compliment _____

On the lines, write the spelling words from the list that are synonyms for the following words.

disorder

14. _____

15. _____

16. _____

fantastic

17. _____

18. _____

19. _____

reliable

20. _____

Apply

On the line, write the spelling word from the list that is related by a common base or root word to each of the following words.

21. hinder _____

22. legal _____

23. picture _____

24. select _____

25. inflame _____

26. feature _____

27. laminate _____

28. logical _____

29. compliment _____

30. legible _____

31. register _____

32. literate _____

33. suppose _____

34. roaring _____

35. consist _____

36. wondering _____

37. tumultuous _____

38. ordinary _____

39. pandemic _____

40. marvel _____

Spelling • *Skills Practice 1*

Name _____ Date _____

Pronouns

Focus

- A **subject pronoun** replaces one or more nouns in the subject. *I, you, he, she, it, we,* and *they* are subject pronouns.

- An **object pronoun** replaces one or more nouns in the predicate. *Me, you, her, him, it, us,* and *them* are object pronouns.

- A **possessive pronoun** shows ownership. *My, your, her, his, our, your, its,* and *their* are used with nouns. *Mine, yours, hers, his, its, ours, yours,* and *theirs* are used alone.

- **They** organized a yard sale. **She** ran to first base.

- Ishiko came with **me** to the concert. Uncle Tito played with **them**. I gave **her** my notes.

- **Your** sister scored a goal. Therese can have **mine**. This last slice of pie is **yours**.

Practice Circle the pronouns in this paragraph.

On our way home from school, Aaron and I almost always stop at the little store about a block from my house. He buys a bottle of soda and nearly finishes it before we even get back outside. I do not like pop. Its flavor is too sugary for me. I usually get a couple of apples, but I eat them slowly. I like knowing that they are a healthful snack.

Apply The sentences below contain misused pronouns. Rewrite each sentence so that it is correct.

1. Mine brother is studying for him college entrance exams.

_____

_____

2. They's shirts got splattered with mud from we's driveway.

_____

_____

3. Us are joining you's class for a field trip to the museum.

_____

_____

4. Me have decided to invite thems to mine's favorite restaurant.

_____

_____

5. It high walls helped protect we from our's enemies.

_____

_____

6. Nina's dad drove she and me to our's dance lessons.

_____

_____

Name _____ Date _____

Comparatives, Superlatives, and the Prefix *re-*

- A **comparative adjective** or **adverb** compares one person, action, or thing to another.

- A **superlative adjective** or **adverb** compares one person, action, or thing to several others.

- When forming the **comparative,** most longer modifiers must be preceded by the word **more.**

- When forming the **superlative,** most longer modifiers must be preceded by the word **most.**

- The prefix *re-* means "again." For example, *reuse* means "to use again."

- I am **taller** now than I was two years ago.

- That is the **prettiest** painting in the museum.

- Tom was **more patient** than Jim.

- Of all the members of her track team, Kyra runs **most quickly.**

Rewrite each sentence below so that it contains a word using the prefix *re-* and a comparative or superlative adjective or adverb.

Example   Emile had to wash the glasses again in the small sink.
Emile had to rewash the glasses in the smallest sink she had ever seen.

1. Suddenly, the rabbit appeared again in the lovely meadow.

_____

2. The good ice cream shop will not open again until next summer.

_____

3. I had to listen to LaTonya tell the pleasant story again.

_____

4. Julio discovered again a large science kit in his closet.

_____

5. Please state your answer again.

_____

Apply Write the comparative and superlative forms for each word.

6. simple _____

7. crowded _____

8. straight _____

9. likely _____

10. early _____

11. smooth _____

12. funny _____

13. powerfully _____

14. dangerously _____

15. difficult _____

Name _____ Date _____

Selection Vocabulary

Focus

flickering (fli' • kər • ing) *adj.* burning or shining in an irregular way (page 190)

expands (ik • spandz') *v.* becomes larger (page 191)

propel (prə • pel') *v.* to cause to move forward (page 191)

gusty (gus' • tē) *adj.* blowing in strong, sudden bursts (page192)

reliable (ri • lī' • ə • bəl) *adj.* able to be depended on (page 192)

revolving doors (ri • vôl' • ving dorz) *n.* plural of **revolving door:** a door at the front of the building that moves in a circle around a central point (page 193)

converts (kən • vûrts') *v.* changes something into something different (page 194)

currents (kûr' • ənts) *n.* plural of **current:** a flow of electricity (page 194)

fossil fuels (fôs' • əl fyoo' • əlz) *n.* plural of **fossil fuel:** a fuel formed from the remains of plants and animals. Coal and petroleum are fossil fuels. (page 195)

economical (ek' • ə • nôm' • i • kəl) *adj.* a good use of resources; not wasteful (page 195)

Practice **Circle the word in parentheses that best fits each sentence.**

1. A solar panel (converts, currents) sunlight into electricity.

2. Please use the (fossil fuels, revolving doors) to enter the building.

3. The suitcase (converts, expands) to hold more clothing.

4. Using coupons and watching for sales are (economical, gusty) ways to shop.

5. Burning (currents, **fossil fuels**) is probably not the best way to create energy.

6. This digital watch is much more (**reliable**, flickering) than my old one.

7. Electrical (revolving doors, **currents**) will not flow through insulating materials.

8. Kicking your legs will help (converts, **propel**) you through the water.

9. I knew the batteries were almost dead when the flashlight began (expands, **flickering**).

10. A (reliable, **gusty**) breeze threatened to capsize the sailboat.

 Write the selection vocabulary word that best answers each question below.

11. Which word describes someone who always shows up on time and never goes back on his or her word? _____

12. Which word describes what a balloon filling with air does?

_____

13. Which word describes water moving in the ocean or electricity moving through a wire? _____

14. A banker changes French francs into American dollars. Which word describes what he does? _____

15. A drooping flag suddenly lifts in a strong breeze. Just as quickly, it droops back down. What kind of wind is blowing? _____

Name _____ Date _____

Cause and Effect

Focus

When one event causes another to happen, the events have a **cause-and-effect relationship.**

- A **cause** is the reason that an event happens.
- An **effect** is the result of a cause.
- Writers use words such as *because, since, therefore,* and *so* to show the reader that a cause-and-effect relationship has taken place.

Practice

On a separate piece of paper, answer the following questions about causes and effects in the story "The Wind at Work."

1. What caused the Dutch to build windmills throughout the flatlands?

2. How did harnessing the wind for power affect working conditions?

3. What caused windmills to become less widely used?

4. What effect would using more wind power have on the environment?

5. What caused humans to begin relying so heavily on fossil fuels?

Apply   One-half of each cause-and-effect relationship is missing in the sentences below. Complete the sentences by providing the missing half.

6. When my alarm rang this morning, _____

_____

7. Highway 56 is closed; therefore, _____

_____

8. Since Annika is bringing a dessert to the party, _____

_____

9. Tucker raised his hand because _____

_____

10. People are not allowed to skateboard there, so _____

_____

11. The entire class began laughing when _____

_____

12. Because my grandparents are visiting this weekend, _____

_____

Name _____ **Date** _____

Persuasive Letter

 **Think** **Audience: Who** will read your persuasive letter?

_____

Purpose: What is your reason for writing a persuasive letter?

_____

_____

 **Prewriting** **Persuasive writing is used to convince someone to agree with your opinion. Use the graphic organizer below to plan your persuasive letter.**

1. Write your viewpoint (main idea).

2. Provide facts, examples, and/or expert opinions that support the viewpoint presented.

3. In addition to providing hard facts, use an emotional appeal that you believe will be effective with the audience.

4. End your letter with a conclusion that restates the viewpoint or solution and asks the reader for action, if appropriate.

Revising   Use this checklist to revise your persuasive letter.

☐ Did you use formal language in your letter and include information that is appropriate for the audience?

☐ Does your letter have clear organization?

☐ Did you use persausive techniques, like emotional appeal, to convince your reader?

☐ Did you avoid using contractions and slang terms?

Editing/Proofreading   Use this checklist to correct mistakes.

☐ Did you follow the correct format for a formal letter?

☐ Did you check all capitalization, punctuation, and spelling?

☐ Have you correctly used compound sentences?

☐ Have you correctly used subjective, objective, and possessive pronouns?

Publishing   Use this checklist to publish your persuasive letter.

☐ Write your letter on a clean sheet of paper, or type your letter on a computer and print it.

☐ Address your envelope, and prepare your letter for sending.

Name _____   **Date** _____

Spelling

Focus
• Understanding and identifying **Greek roots** and their meanings can help you define and spell difficult and unfamiliar words. Here are some of the Greek roots in the spelling words and their meanings:

meter = measure; ***chron*** = time; ***therm*** = heat

Practice   **Write the spelling word that results when the prefix *re-* is added.**

1. apply   _____
2. organize   _____
3. furnish   _____
4. purchase   _____
5. formulate _____
6. introduce _____
7. affirm   _____
8. inforce   _____
9. visit   _____
10. generate _____

Each of the following examples includes at least one Greek root. On the line, write the spelling word that is represented in each of the examples.

11. chron + ological = _____

12. syn + chron + ize = _____

Word List
1. refurnish
2. meter
3. diameter
4. reorganize
5. reintroduce
6. revisit
7. chronic
8. chronicle
9. reaffirm
10. barometer
11. reinforce
12. thermometer
13. reformulate
14. synchronize
15. repurchase
16. chronology
17. regenerate
18. centimeter
19. chronological
20. reapply

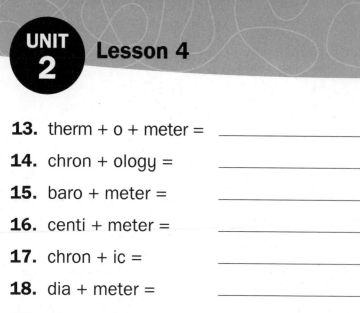

13. therm + o + meter = _____

14. chron + ology = _____

15. baro + meter = _____

16. centi + meter = _____

17. chron + ic = _____

18. dia + meter = _____

19. chron + icle = _____

Which Greek root in the spelling list is a word by itself?

20. _____

Apply **Decide which Greek root, when added, correctly spells the word in each sentence. Write the spelling word on the line.**

21. A _____ometer measures heat. _____

22. My little sister is almost one _____ tall. _____

23. The textbook listed the _____ology of events. _____

24. She suffers from _____ic pain. _____

25. Let's syn _____ize our watches. _____

On the line, write the spelling word that is related by a common base or root word to each of the following words.

26. furnished _____

27. purchasing _____

28. application _____

29. formula _____

30. introduction _____

Name _____   **Date** _____

Regular and Irregular Plurals

Focus   **Most regular plurals** are formed by just adding *-s* or *-es*, but **irregular plurals** do not follow any rules for forming the plural.

- For words that end in a consonant and *y*, change the *y* to *i* and then add *-es*.
- For some words that end in *f* or *fe*, change the *f* or *fe* to *v* and add *-es*.
- For words that end in a consonant and *o*, add either *-s* or *-es*. You must use a dictionary to determine which is correct.
- For some words, the plural form is a different word.
- For some words, the singular and plural forms are the same.

- baby, babies
  fly, flies

- loaf, loaves
  shelf, shelves

- mango, mangos
  potato, potatoes
  rhino, rhinos

- tooth, teeth
  child, children

- deer, deer
  fish, fish

Practice   For each singular word below, write its plural form on the line.

1. floor _____

2. bench _____

3. candy _____

4. loaf _____

5. deer _____

6. journey _____

7. boss _____

8. tooth _____

9. hero _____

10. cliff _____

Apply **Complete each sentence below by writing the plural form of the word in parentheses on the line. Use a dictionary to check your answers.**

11. My _____ helped me rake leaves out of the garden. (friend)

12. How many _____ are in the zoo's aquarium? (fish)

13. Dr. Lynn bought _____ and cucumbers at the market. (tomato)

14. Anna undid the _____ on her suitcase. (latch)

15. They will travel through the mountains and

_____ of Montana. (valley)

16. Several _____ found a way into the pantry. (mouse)

17. We keep the butter _____ in that top drawer. (knife)

18. Can you name all the _____ in Africa? (country)

19. Three _____ waited in line in front of me at the deli. (person)

20. The students' _____ lit up when they heard the news. (face)

21. One night a week, the Alis enjoy watching

_____ together. (video)

22. This book describes the _____ of a few famous inventors. (life)

Name _____ Date _____

Words with Latin Roots and the Prefix *non-*

Focus
- Many words in the English language contain **Latin roots.** For example, *portable, import,* and *porter* all contain the Latin root *port,* which means "to carry." Identifying and understanding Latin roots can help you define difficult words.

- The prefix **non-** means "not." When combined with a base or root word it forms an antonym of that word.

Practice Each word below uses the prefix *non-* and contains a root word. On the line, write the word's definition. As a hint, you have been provided the meaning of each root word. Use a dictionary if you need help.

1. The Latin root *form* means "shape"

   nonconform = _____

2. The Latin root *aqua* means "water"

   nonaquatic = _____

3. The Greek root *bio* means "life"

   nonbiological = _____

4. The Latin root *sens* means "feel"

   nonsensitive = _____

Apply Each group of words uses the same Latin root. Select the correct meaning of the root word from the box, and write it on the line. Write an original sentence using each word.

ray	cut	different	hold

5. variety; variable; various

Latin root *var* means _____

_____

_____

6. radiator; radiation; radio

Latin root *rad* means _____

_____

_____

7. dissect; intersect; section

Latin root *sect* means _____

_____

_____

8. contain; maintain; detain

Latin root *tain* means _____

_____

_____

Word Structure • *Skills Practice 1*

Name _____ **Date** _____

Selection Vocabulary

food chain (fōod chān) *n.* a group of living things that form a chain in which the first living thing is eaten by the second, the second is eaten by the third, and so on (page 204)

food web (fōod web) *n.* a group of food chains in an ecosystem that are connected (page 204)

ecosystem (ē' • kō • sis' • təm) *n.* all the living and nonliving things in a certain area (page 204)

absorbs (əb • sorbz') *v.* takes in (page 205)

algae (al' • jē) *n.* simple living things that are composed of one or more cells; most algae are plants that do not have roots or flowers. (page 208)

ridges (ri' • jəz) *n.* plural of **ridge:** a raised, narrow strip (page 209)

predators (pre' • də • tərz) *n.* plural of **predator:** an animal that hunts and kills other animals for food (page 211)

scavenger (ska' • vən • jər) *n.* an animal that feeds on dead animals (page 211)

omnivores (om' • nə • vorz') *n.* plural of **omnivore:** an animal that eats both animal flesh and plants (page 212)

diet (dī' • it) *n.* the food and drink eaten by an animal (page 212)

If the boldfaced definition given for the underlined word in each sentence is correct, write *T* on the line. If the definition is incorrect, write *F* on the line.

1. The mouse scurried quickly through the field, hoping to avoid <u>predators</u>.

animals that hunt other animals for food _____

2. The pool had not been used in years, so <u>algae</u> covered much of the water's surface.

a kind of tarp or blanket _____

3. A horse's <u>diet</u> consists mainly of roughage and water.

food and drink eaten by an animal _____

4. As we came around the bend, we startled a <u>scavenger</u> that had been eating.

an animal that feeds on dead animals _____

5. Dr. Meredith studied the <u>food chain</u> in Lake Superior.

the different things an animal will eat _____

6. A kitchen sponge <u>absorbs</u> water, but it also breeds bacteria.

cleans or wipes _____

7. The desert <u>ecosystem</u> is more diverse than you might imagine.

all the living and nonliving things in an area _____

8. At times, <u>omnivores</u> become predators.

animals that eat both flesh and plants _____

9. Gum got embedded between the <u>ridges</u> on the bottom of my shoe.

raised, narrow strips _____

10. A rain forest's <u>food web</u> contains many thousands of creatures.

a method animals use to get their food _____

Apply Review the selection vocabulary words for "What Are Food Chains and Webs?". On a separate sheet of paper, write five sentences using at least two vocabulary words from this lesson in each sentence.

Vocabulary • *Skills Practice 1*

Name _____ Date _____

Classify and Categorize

Focus Classifying and categorizing are ways of organizing information. They can help you better understand and remember what you read.

- **Classifying** is identifying the similarities that objects, characters, or events have in common with each other, and then grouping them by their similarities.

- **Categorizing** is the act of organizing the objects, characters, or events into groups, or categories.

Practice Reread pages 210–212 in "What Are Food Chains and Webs?". Animals that eat other animals can be categorized in several different ways. On the lines below, list the seven possible categories the text mentions for animals that eat other animals.

1. _____

2. _____

3. _____

4. _____

5. _____

6. _____

7. _____

Apply Scientific classification is used around the world to classify plants, animals, and other organisms. Every living thing on Earth can be categorized into several groups that range from the very general to the very specific—from kingdoms to species. Classify the animals listed in the box by placing them into their appropriate categories in the chart below.

| chimpanzee | turtle | mouse | alligator | fruit fly |
| ladybug | cobra | horse | praying mantis | |

Kingdom:
Animalia

Class:
Mammalia
(Mammals)

Class:
Reptilia
(Reptiles)

Class:
Insecta
(Insects)

Comprehension Skill • *Skills Practice 1*

Name _____ Date _____

Persuasive Report

Audience: Who will read your persuasive report?

_____

Purpose: What is your reason for writing a persuasive report?

_____

_____

The graphic organizer below will help you outline your persuasive report. Use the numbered lines to provide supporting facts and details for each subtopic.

Topic:

Subtopic:	Subtopic:

1. _____   1. _____

2. _____   2. _____

Subtopic:	Subtopic:

1. _____   1. _____

2. _____   2. _____

Conclusion:

Revising
Use this checklist to revise the draft of your report.

☐ Is your draft organized according to the outline you prepared?

☐ Are your paragraphs cogent?

☐ Have you included facts and details that support and address your opinion?

☐ Do you have strong opening and concluding paragraphs?

☐ Did you use persuasive techniques to convince your reader?

Editing/Proofreading
Use this checklist to correct mistakes.

☐ Have you correctly capitalized proper nouns?

☐ Have you spelled specialized words correctly and consistently throughout your report?

☐ Did you avoid using contractions and slang terms?

Publishing
Use this checklist to share your draft.

☐ Neatly type your persuasive report and put it in your Writing Portfolio.

☐ Read the draft of your report to a group of classmates.

Name _____ Date _____

Spelling

Focus

- Many words feature the prefix **non-,** which usually means "not." It often changes a base word to an antonym.
- Here are some of the **Latin roots** in the spelling words and their meanings:

  sect = cut; **vor** = eat; **carn** = meat; **herb** = "plant"; **jur, jud, jus** = "law"; **omni** = "all"

Practice Remove the prefix *non-* from each word and write the resulting word.

1. nonabrasive _____

2. nonconforming _____

3. noncreative _____

4. nonsense _____

5. nonstick _____

Fill in the appropriate Latin root or Latin root form and write the resulting spelling word on the line.

6. _____ion _____

7. _____isdiction _____

8. de_____ _____

9. _____y _____

10. carni_____e _____

Word List

1. devour
2. nonviolent
3. section
4. nontoxic
5. nonstick
6. jury
7. nonessential
8. carnivore
9. herbivore
10. nonresident
11. dissect
12. intersect
13. noncreative
14. jurist
15. jurisdiction
16. nonsense
17. nonconforming
18. omnivore
19. nonprofit
20. nonabrasive

Apply   **Write the spelling word that matches each definition on the line.**

11. not fierce   _____

12. not important   _____

13. not inventive   _____

14. not a member of a city   _____

15. not sticky   _____

16. not fitting in   _____

17. not taking in gains   _____

18. not rough   _____

19. not poisonous   _____

20. not having meaning   _____

Determine which Latin root correctly completes the word in each sentence. Write the appropriate Latin root and write the resulting spelling word on the lines below.

21. A _____y judges whether a person is guilty or innocent.   _____

22. A _____ivore eats meat.   _____

23. The two streets inter_____ by the gas station.   _____

24. The _____ist did not know if the defendant was guilty.   _____

25. That _____ion of the library holds fiction books.   _____

26. The snake wanted to de_____ the mouse.   _____

27. A giraffe is a herbi_____.   _____

28. The biologist began to dis_____ the frog.   _____

29. I am an _____vore.   _____

30. Which police station has _____diction over our neighborhood?   _____

Name _____   **Date** _____

Possessive Nouns, Possessive Pronouns, and Conjunctions

Focus   **Possessive nouns and pronouns** show ownership.

- Add *'s* to singular nouns and plural nouns that do not end with s to form possessives.

- the pie**'s** flavor
  Chris**'s** textbook
  the children**'s** coats

- Add only an apostrophe to plural nouns that end with s to form possessives.

- students**'** answers
  cities**'** laws

- Possessive pronouns do not need apostrophes. They can be used in front of nouns or by themselves.

- **His** bicycle tire needs air.
  Where is **our** new classroom?
  This pencil is **yours.**

- A **conjunction** is a word that connects words or groups of words. A coordinating conjunction joins words or groups of words that are equally important in a sentence: *and, but, or, so, nor, either, yet,* and *for.*

- **Subordinating conjunctions** connect two clauses where one clause is grammatically dependent on the other: *after, although, before, if,* and *when.*

Practice   Circle the possessive noun or pronoun that correctly completes each sentence below and underline each conjunction.

1. Some of the trees are already beginning to lose (their, their's) leaves, before anyone predicted.

2. (Omars', Omar's) classmates voted for him to become student treasurer, although Jeremy was better in math.

3. Mrs. Riaz signed all her (employees', employee's) checks on the same day, and she never missed anyone.

4. (My, Mine) favorite actor has a new movie coming out soon, but it is not showing in my town.

5. The (runners's, runners') faces dripped with sweat, and they were exhausted.

Apply Use *and, but,* or *or* to complete each sentence below and circle each possessive noun and underline each possessive pronoun.

6. Next year I will have Ms. Patel for my math _____ social studies classes.

7. The Suarezes planned to take Nitesh's boat and go sailing, _____ there was hardly any wind.

8. You need to decide whether we will have pizza, _____ you will make your famous meatloaf.

9. Dana's soccer team will either score on this kick, _____ the game will be over.

10. A door slammed somewhere in the house, _____ then I heard my sister yelling.

11. Tulips, roses, _____ daisies are Faith's favorite flowers.

12. Mountain climbing is a thrilling activity, _____ you need professional training before you can use Tim's gear.

13. I want the Hawks to win in the finals, _____ the Bobcats are expected to win their third title.

14. Dante washed his face, brushed his teeth, _____ combed his hair before leaving the house.

Name _____ Date _____

Irregular Verbs and the Prefix *mid-*

Focus The rule for forming the past tense of most verbs is to add *-ed*. **Irregular verbs** do not follow this rule. Instead you must learn the present tense, past tense, and past participle of each verb.

- For example, *run* and *ran* are different by only one letter, but *go* and *went* are completely different words.

- The prefix **mid-** means "at or in the middle of." For example, *midsection* means the section in the middle.

Practice Use the tense shown at the end of the sentence to decide which irregular verb correctly completes the sentence. Circle the correct choice. Underline the words in the sentences that contain the prefix *mid-.*

1. Most colonists (feel, felt) _____ strongly about their British rulers. **PAST**

2. In wartime it is often difficult to (found, find)

_____ normal, everyday items. **PRESENT**

3. Midway through the final quarter, he (leave, left)

_____ the football game to avoid traffic. **PAST**

4. He (come, came) _____ at the midpoint of the conflict to give aid to the Patriots. **PAST**

5. I (have, had) _____ never worked past midnight. **PRESENT**

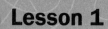 

Apply The following paragraphs contain incorrect past-tense verbs. On the line, write the correct past-tense form for each irregular verb.

Last summer my family and I **goed** _____

to Philadelphia. When the trip **beginned** _____

it was raining, but by the time we stopped for lunch, the sun

had **fighted** _____ its way through the clouds.

At Independence Hall the tour guide **telled**

_____ us the story of the Declaration of

Independence. Afterward I **buyed** _____ a

postcard from the gift shop. I **writed** _____

to my grandmother, telling her about everything we had seen

so far. My dad **thinked** _____ the postcard

was a thoughtful thing to do.

We **spended** _____ the next afternoon

watching a baseball game. The best part was when my

dad **catched** _____ a ball that was hit

into the stands. After we left the stadium, Dad **gived**

_____ it to my brother.

I **bringed** _____ my camera on the trip

and **taked** _____ a lot of pictures. Sometime

I will show them to you.

UNIT **3** Lesson 1

Name _____ Date _____

Selection Vocabulary

Focus

colonies (ko' • lə • nēz) *n.* plural of **colony:** a territory ruled by another country (page 230)

loyal (loi' • əl) *adj.* having or showing strong and lasting support for someone or something (page 231)

settlers (set' • lərz) *n.* plural of **settler:** a person who makes his or her home in a new land or country (page 233)

protest (prō' • test) *n.* an objection to (page 234)

liberty (lib' • ər • tē) *n.* freedom from control of another country (page 236)

militia (mə • lish' • ə) *n.* a group of citizens trained to fight and help in emergencies (page 239)

necessities (nə • ses' • i • tēz) *n.* plural of **necessity:** something that is needed (page 243)

pamphlets (pam' • flitz) *n.* plural of **pamphlet:** a small book that has a paper cover (page 244)

published (pub' • lisht) *v.* past tense of **publish:** to print a newspaper, magazine, book, or other material and offer it for sale (page 244)

discharge (dis' • chärj) *n.* dismissal from service or a job (page 248)

Practice Write the selection vocabulary word that best fits each clue below.

1. Dogs are often described with this word.

   Which word is it? _____

2. When people do this, sometimes they make signs, gather in large groups, or sign petitions. What is it?

   _____

3. Many people fought very long and hard for this.

   What is it? _____

4. This is a word used when someone is let go from a job.

Which word is it? _____

5. The United States was originally made of thirteen of these.

What are they? _____

6. This word describes water, clothing, and food.

Which word is it? _____

7. These could help you give information to other people.

What are they? _____

8. This group of people is trained to help others in an emergency.

Which word describes them? _____

9. These people make their homes in new lands.

They are _____.

10. This word describes printed materials for sale to the public.

Which word is it? _____

 On a separate sheet of paper, create five sentences using the selection vocabulary words. Each sentence should contain at least two vocabulary words. Make sure to use each word at least once.

Name _____ **Date** _____

Cause and Effect

When one event causes another to happen, the events have a **cause-and-effect relationship.**

- A cause is the reason that an event happens.
- An effect is the result of the cause.
- Writers use words such as *because, since, therefore,* and *so* to show the reader that a cause-and-effect relationship has taken place.

Review the selection ". . . If You Lived at the Time of the American Revolution" to find out why the following events happened. Write down the cause for each event.

1. The Patriots dumped England's tea into Boston Harbor because

_____.

2. The British soldiers were called Redcoats because

_____.

3. Many families were split because

_____.

4. Certain soldiers in the Continental Army were called minutemen because

_____.

5. During the war, paper money lost value because

_____.

UNIT
3
Lesson 1

Apply The sentences below are incomplete. Each sentence shows only one half of a cause-and-effect relationship. At the beginning of each sentence, write *C* if you are given the cause. Write *E* if you are given the effect. Then, complete the sentence by adding the missing half.

6. _____ The front tire of Reggie's bicycle was flat, so

_____.

7. _____ Monika grabbed an umbrella as she left home because

_____.

8. _____ Since our soccer team won nearly all its games,

_____.

9. _____ Sophie has books due at the library; therefore

_____.

10. _____ A section of our street is closed because

_____.

Now write your own cause-and-effect sentences using *therefore, since, because,* and *so*.

_____

_____

_____

_____

_____

_____

Comprehension Skill • *Skills Practice 1*

Name _____ **Date** _____

Recording Concept Information

As I read the selection, this is what I added to my understanding of the unit theme Making a New Nation.

• ". . . If You Lived at the Time of the American Revolution" by Kay Moore

_____

_____

• "The Midnight Ride of Paul Revere" by Henry Wadsworth Longfellow

_____

_____

• "The Master Spy of Yorktown" by Burke Davis

_____

_____

• "Shh! We're Writing the Constitution" by Jean Fritz

_____

_____

• "Give Me Liberty!" by Russell Freedman

_____

_____

Name _____ **Date** _____

Knowledge About Making a New Nation

- This is what I know about making a new nation before reading the unit.

_____

_____

_____

_____

_____

_____

- These are some things about making a new nation that I would like to talk about and understand better.

_____

_____

_____

_____

_____

_____

Reminder: I should read this page again when I get to the end of the unit to see how much my ideas about making a new nation have changed.

Name _____ **Date** _____

Ideas About Making a New Nation

Of the ideas discussed in class about making a new nation,
these are the ones I found most interesting.

Ideas About Making a New Nation (continued)

Write down the ideas you found most interesting about the selection ". . . If You Lived at the Time of the American Revolution." Discuss your ideas with the class.

Lesson 1

Name _____ **Date** _____

Timed Writing: Persuasive Writing

Think

Audience: Who will read your persuasive writing?

_____

Purpose: Why are you writing to persuade?

_____

_____

In school, you may be given only a short amount of time to write an essay or a paragraph. Your first step should always be to read the directions carefully. For the assignment below, circle the most important information in the directions. Then, list three ideas you might write about to complete the assignment.

Write a persuasive paragraph about a rule or law that you think is unfair. Be sure to include at least three sentences supporting your argument. Also include one sentence that tells the opposite point of view. You have twenty minutes to complete the paragraph.

1. _____

2. _____

3. _____

_____

Revising

Use this checklist to revise your persuasive paragraph.

☐ Did you clearly state your opinion in the opening sentence?

☐ Did you include three sentences supporting your argument?

☐ Did you include one sentence about the opposite point of view?

☐ Did you use formal language?

Editing/Proofreading

Use this checklist to correct mistakes.

☐ Are there any spelling errors?

☐ Have you used adjectives to modify nouns and pronouns?

☐ Do all the sentences contain correct punctuation?

☐ Have you corrected any contractions?

Publishing

Use this checklist to prepare your persuasive paragraph for publication.

☐ If you have time, rewrite your paragraph neatly on a fresh sheet of paper.

☐ Hand in your completed Timed Writing assignment.

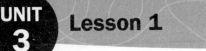

UNIT 3 Lesson 1

Name _____   Date _____

Spelling

Focus

• When you add the inflectional ending **-ed** to a verb, it forms the past tense. Drop the *e* if a word ends in *e*, and then add the *-ed* ending. If the word ends in a short vowel followed by a single consonant, then double the consonant.

• **Irregular verbs** are verbs that do not form the past tense by adding *-ed: choose, chose; forbid, forbade; creep, crept.* Knowing the past tense of irregular verbs will help you prevent spelling mistakes.

• A prefix changes the meaning of the base word it precedes. Identifying prefixes and understanding their meanings can help you figure out the meaning and spelling of a difficult or unfamiliar word. The prefix **mid-** means "the middle." It does not change the spelling of the base word to which it is added.

Word List

1. *midnight*
2. *chose*
3. *escaped*
4. *midyear*
5. *choose*
6. *downloaded*
7. *midsection*
8. *forbid*
9. *forbade*
10. *graduated*
11. *midterm*
12. *midstream*
13. *creep*
14. *crept*
15. *financed*
16. *communicated*
17. *midfield*
18. *midland*
19. *employed*
20. *midsummer*

Practice   Add the inflectional ending *-ed* to the following base words and write the resulting spelling words on the lines.

1. download   _____

2. employ   _____

3. communicate   _____

4. graduate   _____

5. finance   _____

6. escape   _____

Write the present tense and past tense of the irregular verbs in the spelling list.

	Present	**Past**
7.	_____	_____
8.	_____	_____
9.	_____	_____

Add the prefix *mid-* to the following base words and write the resulting spelling words on the lines.

10. land _____   **14.** field _____

11. year _____   **15.** summer _____

12. night _____   **16.** section _____

13. stream _____   **17.** term _____

 Apply **If the underlined verb in the sentence is incorrect, write the correct form of the verb from the spelling list on the line. If it is correct, write correct.**

18. Yesterday, I <u>forbidded</u> him to leave.   _____

19. We <u>downloadded</u> that new game last week.   _____

20. We never <u>communicatted</u> very well.   _____

21. The couple <u>financed</u> their car payment.   _____

22. The store <u>employed</u> ten people.   _____

23. The sisters <u>creppt</u> downstairs.   _____

24. The mouse <u>escapped</u> from the cat.   _____

Name _____ Date _____

Comparative and Superlative Adjectives and Adverbs

Focus

Rule	Example
• A **comparative adjective** or **adverb** compares one person, thing, or action to another.	• I am **taller** now than I was two years ago.
• A **superlative adjective** or **adverb** compares one person, thing, or action to several others.	• That is the **prettiest** painting in the museum.
• For most longer modifiers use the word *more* for the comparative, or *most*, for the superlative instead of the *-er* or *-est* endings.	• Tom was **more patient** than Jim. Of all her team members, Kyra runs **most quickly.**

Practice Write the comparative and superlative forms of each adjective and adverb listed below.

1. quiet _____

2. crispy _____

3. hot _____

4. soon _____

5. excited _____

6. slowly _____

7. interesting _____

Cross out the incorrect form of each comparative or superlative adjective or adverb in each sentence. Then, write the correct form on the line that follows.

8. The three-toed sloth moves the slowliest of all

    land mammals. _____

9. The koala is more fast than the three-toed sloth, but only

    when it is awake. _____

10. Koalas spend about twenty-two hours a day sleeping,
    making them the more sleepy of all of animals.

    _____

11. The capybara, a rodent that can weigh more than one
    hundred pounds, is definitely heaviest than an

    average mouse. _____

12. The black mamba's speed and deadly bite make it the

    world's dangerest snake. _____

13. At one hundred fifty years, the reptile that lives most
    longly is the Galapagos tortoise.

    _____

14. The world's largerest spider has a perfect name—the

    Goliath birdeater. _____

15. With a wingspan of thirteen feet, the Marabou stork has
    the most widest wingspan of all birds.

    _____

Name _____ Date _____

Homophones and the Suffix *-less*

Focus | Homophones are words that sound the same but have different spellings and meanings. The following word pairs are examples of homophones.

| there | for | would | so | made | wear |
| there | four | wood | sew | maid | where |

there   for   would   so   made   wear

their   four   wood   sew   maid   where

Many words feature the suffix *-less.* This suffix means "without" when added to base or root words.

    Hope + less = without hope

    Fear + less = without fear

Practice | **Fill in the blank in each sentence with the appropriate homophone.**

rose	rows	threw	through

1. At the end of the school year, I gave a single red

_____ to my favorite teacher, Ms. Mendoza.

2. All the _____ were filled with people awaiting the performance.

3. The crowd cheered when the quarterback _____ a touchdown in the final seconds of the game.

4. The Millers will have to travel _____ the mountains to reach their new home.

Write the word on the line that corresponds with the definition.

baseless	tireless	careless
powerless	seamless	thoughtless

5. Without seams or interruptions _____

6. Without thought _____

7. Without a care _____

8. Without getting tired _____

9. Without a base or foundation for a thought _____

10. Identify the two base words that are also homophones. Provide the other half of the homophone pair.

_____

_____

Apply **Each underlined word is part of a homophone group. Write another word from the homophone group on the line. Provide a matching homophone and then write a sentence using it correctly.**

11. Then he said, "Good Night!" and with muffled oar

    Silently <u>rowed</u> to the Charleston shore _____

    _____

12. A line of black that bends and floats

    On the rising <u>tide</u>, like a bridge of boats. _____

    _____

Name _____ Date _____

Selection Vocabulary

Focus

aloft (ə • lôft') *adv.* far above the ground (page 259)

muffled (muf' • əld) *adj.* made softer or less loud (page 259)

magnified (mag' • ni • fīd) *v.* past tense of **magnify**: to make something look bigger than it really is (page 259)

sentinel (sen' • tə • nəl) *n.* a sentry (page 260)

mount (mount) *v.* to get up on a horse (page 261)

gleam (glēm) *n.* a flash or beam of light (page 261)

ledge (lej) *n.* a narrow surface on a cliff or rock wall (page 263)

weathercock (weth' • ər • kôk') *n.* a weathervane (page 264)

assigned (ə • sīnd') *v.* past tense of **assign**: to give out as a task (page 269)

spread (spred) *v.* to make or become known by more people (page 269)

Practice Write the word from the word box that matches each definition below.

gleam	mount	muffled	magnified	ledge
assigned	weathercock	aloft	spread	sentinel

1. _____ a flash or beam of light

2. _____ made something look bigger than it really is

3. _____ far above the ground

4. _____ to make or become known by more people

5. _____ a narrow surface on a cliff or rock wall

6. _____ a sentry

7. _____ to get on

8. _____ gave out as a task

9. _____ a weathervane

10. _____ wrapped or covered to soften the sound
    or to protect

Apply **Circle the word in parentheses that best fits each sentence.**

11. The sound of the plane was (muffled/assigned), but we still heard it.

12. Michael slowly crawled across the snowy (ledge/weathercock).

13. The balloon was held (aloft/muffled) by the wind.

14. The news will (spread/mount) quickly to the rest of the family.

15. Let's (witness/mount) our horses and ride through the meadow.

16. The (gleam/ledge) of the car blinded me.

Name _____ **Date** _____

Formulating Questions and Problems

A good question or problem to investigate:

_____

_____

_____

_____

_____

Why this is an interesting question or problem:

_____

_____

_____

_____

Some other things I wonder about this question or problem:

_____

_____

_____

_____

Formulating Questions and Problems (continued)

My investigation group's question or problem:

_____

_____

_____

_____

_____

What our investigation will contribute to the rest of the class:

_____

_____

_____

_____

_____

Some other things I wonder about this question or problem:

_____

_____

_____

_____

_____

Inquiry • *Skills Practice 1*

Name _____ Date _____

Timed Writing: Expository Writing

Think

Audience: Who will read your expository writing?

_____

Purpose: What do you want to tell with your expository writing?

_____

Prewriting

Use the Timed Writing Strategies to complete the following assignment. Start by circling the key things you are asked to do in the instructions. Then, list three details you want to include in your expository writing.

Write a paragraph about your favorite hobby. Be sure to include at least one sentence that describes when you first started doing this activity. Also include two sentences that tell why you enjoy it. You have twenty minutes to complete the assignment.

1. _____

_____

2. _____

_____

3. _____

_____

Revising   Use this checklist to revise your expository writing.

☐ Did you clearly describe your first time doing the activity?

☐ Did your sentences show the reader why it is your favorite hobby?

☐ Did you use transition words to organize your paragraph?

Editing/Proofreading   Use this checklist to correct mistakes.

☐ Are there any spelling errors?

☐ Do all sentences contain correct punctuation?

☐ Did you correctly use prepositions and prepositional phrases?

Publishing   Use this checklist to prepare your expository writing for publication.

☐ If you have time, rewrite your paragraph neatly on a fresh sheet of paper.

☐ Hand in your completed Timed Writing assignment.

Name _____ **Date** _____

Spelling

Focus

- **Irregular plurals** do not follow the regular rules for forming plurals. They do not end in -s or -es. Sometimes the base word spelling changes to form the plural, and sometimes it does not change at all: *child, children; salmon, salmon; person, people*

- **Compound words** consist of two smaller words that have been combined to form one larger word. These two words keep the same spelling in the compound word.

- Understanding and identifying suffixes and their meanings can help you determine the meaning and spelling of a difficult or unfamiliar word. Many words feature the suffix **-less**. *Less* is a word on its own, but is also a suffix that means "without."

Word List

1. children
2. moonlight
3. noiseless
4. shoemaker
5. salmon
6. wastebasket
7. sleeveless
8. halfway
9. people
10. earsplitting
11. sightless
12. quarterfinal
13. countless
14. tombstone
15. stainless
16. letterhead
17. tireless
18. flyswatter
19. friendless
20. showerhead

Practice The following spelling words are missing one of their base words. Write the missing part of the compound word in the space provided.

1. _____ swatter

2. tomb _____

3. _____ final

4. _____ way

5. ear _____

6. letter _____

7. _____basket

8. shower_____

9. _____maker

10. _____light

On the line, write the spelling word that is formed by adding the suffix -less to each of the following base words.

11. friend _____

12. stain _____

13. sleeve _____

14. noise _____

15. tire _____

16. count _____

17. sight _____

Apply   **On the line, write the spelling word that matches each definition.**

18. without sound _____

19. without marks or dirt _____

20. without buddies or pals _____

21. with a lot of energy _____

22. too many to count _____

23. without the ability to see _____

24. without sleeves _____

Name _____ Date _____

Prepositions and Prepositional Phrases

Focus

A **preposition** shows the relationship between a noun or a pronoun and another word in a sentence.

A **prepositional phrase** is a group of words that begins with a preposition and ends with the object of the preposition.

Example

• We walked **through the blinding snowstorm.**

Practice Circle the prepositional phrases in this paragraph.

Individual Chinese kingdoms began building what would become the Great Wall around the seventh century B.C. The wall was started in the northern part of the kingdom's capital. Other states started building walls for protection during the sixth century. In the third century B.C., the first emperor of China connected the walls into one system. The Great Wall extends 4,160 miles across China's countryside. Many tourists today still visit what remains of the wall.

Apply **Write sentences using these prepositions in a prepositional phrase.**

1. after _____

2. at _____

3. from _____

4. on _____

5. under _____

6. with _____

Improve the paragraph below by adding at least four prepositional phrases to provide more information to the reader.

Jonah likes to skateboard. He often goes with his brother.

They prefer the lot next to the big oak trees. Many kids come

here to skate. There is a lot of competition. However, they

also enjoy teaching each other new tricks they learned. Their

parents sometimes sit and watch them skate.

Name _____ Date _____

Base Word Families, Suffixes *-ment, -able, -ful*

Focus

A **base word** can take many different forms when different prefixes, suffixes, and roots are added. When you know the meaning of the base word, you can begin to find the meanings of the words in the base word family.

- The suffix *-ment* means "an action or process, or the result of an action or process." The suffix usually forms nouns as in *government*.

- The suffix *-able* means "capable, having, or worthy of." *Reliable* means "one capable of being relied upon."

- The suffix *-ful* means "full of." *Beautiful* means "full of beauty."

Practice

The following words are followed by their base words. Write three more words with the same base word. Use the suffix listed in one of the derivatives. Use a dictionary if you need help.

1. discovered (-able)
Base word: cover

_____

2. agreed (-ment)
Base word: agree

_____

3. entrusted (-ful)
Base word: trust

_____

4. meaning (-ful)
Base word: mean

_____

Apply Now write two sentences for each base word family. Use the base word in the first sentence and one of the derived words in the second sentence.

5. cover: _____

_____

word in the same family: _____

_____

6. agree: _____

_____

word in the same family: _____

_____

7. trust: _____

_____

word in the same family: _____

_____

8. mean: _____

_____

word in the same family: _____

_____

Name _____ Date _____

Selection Vocabulary

Focus

looting (lōot' • ing) *v.* stealing valuable things from others (page 280)

commander (kə • man' • dər) *n.* a leader (page 280)

invaders (in • vād' • ərz) *n.* plural of **invader:** a person who breaks into something or some place without being asked or wanted (page 280)

prompt (prompt) *adj.* quick or on time (page 281)

civilians (sə • vil' • yənz) *n.* plural of **civilian:** a person not in the military (page 284)

revealing (ri • vēl' • ing) *v.* making known (page 285)

idle (ī' • dəl) *adj.* not busy (page 285)

lessen (les' • ən) *v.* to make or become less (page 287)

precautions (pri • kô' • shənz) *n.* plural of **precaution:** something done beforehand to prevent harm or danger (page 287)

portrait (por' • trit) *n.* a likeness of a person that is created by a painter or photographer (page 291)

Practice

Tell whether the boldfaced definition that is given for the underlined word in each sentence below makes sense. Circle *Yes* or *No.*

1. Our <u>commander</u> let us finish the training early.
   leader .... Yes No

2. Lily was <u>idle</u> while the rest of us worked hard.
   quick or on time .... Yes No

3. I hope the doctor can <u>lessen</u> the pain in my back.
   to make or become less .... Yes No

4. The men were <u>looting</u> the art museum.
   stealing valuable things from others .... Yes No

5. Lorna is taking <u>precautions</u> against getting a sunburn.
something done beforehand to prevent harm or danger .... Yes   No

6. We had <u>prompt</u> service at the new restaurant.
not busy .... Yes   No

7. The <u>invaders</u> destroyed every house on the block.
people not in the armed forces.................................... Yes   No

8. I painted a <u>portrait</u> of my grandfather.
a likeness of a person created by a painter or photographer....... Yes   No

9. The coach is <u>revealing</u> the new quarterback.
hiding .... Yes   No

10. <u>Civilians</u> cheered the Confederate Army as they marched through town.
armed forces .... Yes   No

Apply   **Circle the correct word that completes each sentence.**

11. John gave a _____ answer to the teacher.
a. prompt   **b.** invaders   **c.** mates

12. The ice should _____ the swelling in your ankle.
a. lessen   **b.** idle   **c.** prompt

13. The thieves are _____ and breaking windows.
a. idle   **b.** looting   **c.** revealing

14. The army asked the _____ to leave the area by midnight.
a. civilians   **b.** genius   **c.** portrait

15. Jordan is _____ the ending to the movie!
a. looting   **b.** mutually   **c.** revealing

Name _____ **Date** _____

Drawing Conclusions

Focus Writers do not always provide complete descriptions or detailed information about a topic, character, thing, or event, so readers must draw their own conclusions.

• **Drawing Conclusions** requires readers to make statements about topics, events, characters, or things based on information from the text.

Practice Skim the selection "The Master Spy of Yorktown." Then, next to each person's name below, write a statement (draw a conclusion) about him. Then, record the text clues on which you based your conclusions.

The Marquis de Lafayette: _____

Clues: _____

_____

_____

_____

James Armistead: _____

Clues: _____

_____

_____

_____

Apply Write about a character, topic, thing, or event. Before you begin writing, identify a specific conclusion about your subject that you want readers to draw. Write a paragraph about your subject below. Then, exchange papers with a partner. When you have finished reading each other's papers, write a conclusion you have drawn and the text clues that support it at the bottom of the page.

_____

_____

_____

_____

_____

_____

_____

_____

_____

_____

_____

_____

Conclusion and Text Clues: _____

_____

_____

_____

_____

Name _____ **Date** _____

Making Conjectures

Our question or problem:

_____

_____

_____

_____

_____

Conjecture (my first theory or explanation):

_____

_____

_____

_____

_____

_____

_____

_____

_____

As you collect information, your conjecture will change. Return to this page to record your new theories or explanations about your question or problem.

Establishing Investigation Needs

My group's question or problem:

_____

_____

_____

_____

_____

Knowledge Needs—Information I need to find or figure out in order to investigate the question or problem:

A. _____

B. _____

C. _____

D. _____

E. _____

Source	Useful?	How?
Encyclopedias		
Books		
Magazines		
Newspapers		
Videotapes, filmstrips, and Audio clips		
Television		
Interviews, observations		
Museums		
Other:		

Name _____ **Date** _____

Timed Writing: Summarizing

Think

Audience: Who will read your summary?

_____

Purpose: What is your reason for writing a summary?

_____

Prewriting Use the Timed Writing Strategies to complete the following assignment. Start by circling the key things you are asked to do in the instructions. Then record three details from the selection that you want to include in your summary.

Reread page 291 of "The Master Spy of Yorktown." Write

a short paragraph summarizing the main idea contained

on that page. Be sure to include at least three of the most

important facts or events. You have twenty minutes to

complete this exercise.

1. _____

_____

2. _____

_____

3. _____

_____

Revising   Use this checklist to revise your expository writing.

☐ Did you include a topic sentence at the beginning of your paragraph?

☐ Did you include only the most important details?

☐ Did you use your own words? Are any of your sentences too similar to those in the original selection?

Editing/Proofreading   Use this checklist to correct mistakes.

☐ Did you check the spellings of proper names or specialized words against the original selection?

☐ Do all sentences contain correct punctuation?

☐ Are all prefixes, suffixes, and verb endings used correctly?

☐ Have you correctly used prepositions and prepositional phrases?

Publishing   Use this checklist to prepare your expository writing for publication.

☐ If you have time, rewrite your paragraph neatly on a fresh sheet of paper.

☐ Hand in your completed Timed Writing assignment.

Name _____ **Date** _____

Spelling

Focus

- Understanding and identifying suffixes and their meanings can help you determine the meaning and spelling of a difficult or unfamiliar word. The suffix **-able** means "inclined to," or "capable or worthy of."

- The suffix **-ful** means "full of." The suffixes -ful and -able both make the words to which they are added adjectives.

- The suffix **-ment** means "result or process," or "state or quality of," and is added to verbs to form nouns. When a suffix begins with a consonant, the base word usually does not change when the suffix is added, unless it ends with a y.

Word List

1. dependable
2. movement
3. beautiful
4. peaceful
5. experiment
6. reliable
7. reasonable
8. government
9. helpful
10. fearful
11. embankment
12. entertainment
13. agreeable
14. memorable
15. development
16. thoughtful
17. fruitful
18. fashionable
19. encampment
20. marketable

Practice Add the suffixes -able, -ful, or -ment to the following base words or word parts and write the resulting spelling words on the lines.

1. embank _____

2. reason _____

3. thought _____

4. fear _____

5. help _____

6. fashion _____

7. beauty _____

8. experi _____

9. encamp _____

10. market _____

11. fruit _____

12. entertain _____

13. agree _____

14. govern _____

15. peace _____

16. develop _____

17. depend _____

18. move _____

19. memory _____

20. rely _____

Apply   Match each word to its definition.

21. dependable _____

22. movement _____

23. beautiful _____

24. peaceful _____

25. experiment _____

26. reasonable _____

27. fearful _____

28. embankment _____

29. entertainment _____

30. thoughtful _____

31. fruitful _____

32. fashionable _____

33. encampment _____

34. marketable _____

A. full of beauty

B. state or quality of being amused

C. able to be sold

D. state or quality of being in motion

E. full of fruit

F. full of consideration

G. full of fright

H. able to have confidence in

I. full of calm

J. process of testing

K. result of making camp

L. result of building a raised structure

M. inclined toward clothing trends

N. inclined towards clear thinking

Name _____ Date _____

Electronic Technology: Creating Text

Focus

Today, most people write using word-processing programs. Creating a text is faster and easier to do once you have learned how to use **electronic technology.** Many schools and libraries have computers with word-processing programs available to the students.

Practice

Write about a classmate's favorite movie or book. First, choose someone to interview. Then listen carefully as he or she describes the plot of the movie or book. Be sure to ask questions to discover why your classmate liked the movie or book. Use the following lines to take notes.

_____

_____

_____

_____

_____

_____

_____

_____

_____

_____

Apply Now use a word-processing program to write a paragraph about the movie or book. Be sure to tell why it is your classmate's favorite work. When you have finished, print your paragraph and read it to the class. Use the following lines to write an outline for the electronic text you will create.

_____

_____

_____

_____

_____

_____

_____

_____

_____

_____

_____

_____

_____

_____

Name _____ Date _____

Plurals and the Prefix *con-*

Practice

Complete the following list by filling in the blanks with the correct singular or plural form of each word. Circle the words that contain the prefix *con-*.

	Singular	Plural		Singular	Plural
1.	month	_____	**6.**	_____	ideas
2.	_____	confederations	**7.**	wish	_____
3.	consequence	_____	**8.**	boss	_____
4.	fox	_____	**9.**	conjunction	_____
5.	_____	citizens	**10.**	_____	heroes

Write the word with the prefix *con-* on the line corresponding to its definition.

concede	consequence	contend
constrain	context	confederation

11. Joined with a group of states

_____

12. To force with restrictions in a strained or

difficult manner _____

13. The joining of text together so that it can

show its meaning _____

14. To cede, or yield, with hesitance

_____

15. To struggle with _____

16. A conclusion made with logic, or following a

sequence of events _____

UNIT 3 Lesson 4

Name _____ Date _____

Selection Vocabulary

Focus

character (kâr' • ək • tər) *n.* all the qualities that make a person or thing different from others (page 302)

allegiance (ə • lē' • jəns) *n.* faithful support of a country, person, group, or cause (page 303)

central (sen' • trəl) *adj.* main; chief (page 303)

delegates (de' • li • gəts) *n.* plural of **delegate:** a person who is chosen to act for others (page 303)

concern (kən • sûrn') *n.* something important to a person (page 303)

league (lēg) *n.* a number of people, groups, or countries joined together for a common purpose (page 304)

contribute (kən • trib' • yo͞ot) *v.* to give (page 304)

eavesdroppers (ēvz' • drop' • ərz) *n.* plural of **eavesdropper:** a person who listens to other people talk without letting them know he or she is listening (page 308)

accomplishment (ə • kom' • plish • ment) *n.* achievement (page 309)

rumors (ro͞o' • mərz) *n.* plural of **rumor:** a story or statement passed from one person to another as truth with no proof (page 309)

Practice Write the vocabulary word next to the group of words that have a similar meaning.

1. stories; gossip _____

2. loyalty; support _____

3. busybodies; listeners _____

4. main; most important; major _____

5. donate; give; volunteer _____

6. group; confederation _____

7. achievement; success _____

8. important; worry _____

9. representative; person chosen _____

10. quality; personality _____

Apply

Match each word on the left to its definition on the right.

11. league

12. eavesdroppers

13. central

14. delegates

15. accomplishment

16. concern

17. character

18. contribute

a. main; chief

b. a number of people, groups, or countries joined together for a common purpose

c. something important to a person

d. to give

e. people who are chosen to act for others

f. people who listen to other people talk without letting them know they are listening

g. all the qualities that make a person or thing different from others

h. achievement

Name _____ Date _____

Research Report

 Think

Audience: Who will read your research report?

_____

Purpose: What is your reason for writing a research report?

_____

 **Prewriting**

Note cards will help you organize the answers you find. On each card, record the details you will need later for your bibliography. Fill in the sample index card below to practice.

> ### Bill of Rights
> First Amendment— Freedom of speech, freedom of press, freedom of religion, freedom of peaceable assembly, freedom to petition the government
>
> Second Amendment— right to bear arms
>
> Third Amendment— prevents government from quartering soldiers
>
> Fourth Amendment— unreasonable search and seizure

Question: _____

Answers: _____

Type of source: _____

Author: _____

Title: _____

Pub. City: _____

Pub. Name: _____

Pub. Date: _____

Pages: _____

Revising
Use this checklist to revise your note cards.

- ☐ Did you rewrite the information you found in your own words?
- ☐ Did you include bibliographic information for each source?
- ☐ Did you use clear subject headings?

Editing/Proofreading
Use this checklist to correct mistakes.

- ☐ Did you use quotation marks if you needed to quote an author's exact words?
- ☐ Did you check the spellings of proper names or specialized words against the original selection?
- ☐ Did you check proper nouns and quotations to make sure they are capitalized correctly?

Publishing
Use this checklist to see if you are ready to begin writing your report.

- ☐ Do your note cards contain enough facts, examples, and explanations for you to be able to write an informative research report?
- ☐ Are your note cards organized so that your report will have a beginning, middle, and end?

Name _____   Date _____

Spelling

Focus

• A prefix changes the meaning of the base word it precedes. Identifying prefixes and understanding their meanings can help you figure out the meaning and spelling of a difficult or unfamiliar word. The prefix **con-** means "with," or "together."

• The inflectional ending **-ing** is used in the participial form of verbs. These words can function as verbs, adjectives, or nouns. If a word ends in e, drop the e before adding the inflectional ending -ing. If a word ends in a y or x, the spelling of the base word stays the same when you add the inflectional ending -ing.

Practice   On the line, write the spelling word that results when the prefix *con-* is added to the following base words or word parts.

1. cede   _____

2. cave   _____

3. form   _____

4. current _____

5. clusions _____

6. strain   _____

7. firm   _____

8. front   _____

9. dense   _____

10. figure _____

Word List

1. conform
2. conclusions
3. substituting
4. relaxing
5. concurrent
6. engineering
7. condense
8. liquidating
9. reducing
10. constrain
11. confirm
12. discharging
13. memorizing
14. delegating
15. configure
16. devastating
17. concave
18. marrying
19. concede
20. confront

On the lines, write the spelling words that drop the final *e* before adding the inflectional ending *-ing*.

11. _____   15. _____

12. _____   16. _____

13. _____   17. _____

14. _____

On the lines, write the spelling words whose base words do not change when adding the inflectional ending *-ing*.

18. _____

19. _____

20. _____

 On the line, write the spelling word that is related by a common base or root word to each of the following words.

21. inform _____   31. conceding _____

22. relaxation _____   32. cave _____

23. reduction _____   33. discharge _____

24. liquid _____   34. substitute _____

25. strained _____   35. current _____

26. front _____   36. engineer _____

27. married _____   37. devastate _____

28. conclude _____   38. condensation _____

29. confirmation _____   39. delegate _____

30. memory _____   40. figure _____

Name _____ Date _____

Capitalization

Focus

- Quotations are capitalized when they are complete sentences or when they begin sentences.

- Always capitalize proper nouns, even when they are used as adjectives.

- Personal titles are capitalized only when they are part of a name.

- *A, an, the, but, and, to,* and *of* are not capitalized in titles unless they are the first or last word.

- Patrick Henry is remembered for saying, "Give me liberty, or give me death."

- Swiss watch
  Franklin stove

- my grandpa, our president
  Grandpa Miller,
  President Ford

- *In the Heat of the Night*
  Articles of Confederation
  Everything on a Waffle

Practice Circle the words that should begin with a capital letter.

1. the fourth of july celebrates the signing of the declaration of independence.

2. our first president, general george washington, said: "it is better to offer no excuse than a bad one."

3. one of the few movies made about the american revolution is *drums along the mohawk.*

4. the book *come to the cowpens!* describes a battle between american and british forces.

5. a painting of benjamin franklin hangs in the national portrait gallery in washington, d.c.

Apply   Draw three lines under each letter that should
have been capitalized. Draw a slash through each
letter that should not have been capitalized.

My brother, Brian, attends Thomas Jefferson high school.
He is on the Soccer Team. Each labor day, a fundraiser is
held to raise money for the Jefferson patriots' sports teams.
Tables filled with donated items line the High School's
hallways. Everything is for sale. The high school's Principal,
Henry Showalter, kicked off the event by announcing, "let the
sale begin!"

While the sale was happening inside, games and other
activities were being held on the High School's front lawn. My
brother's Coach sat in the dunking booth for a while. Brian took
his chance, and his second toss sent coach Harris splashing
into the water. It was the funniest thing I have ever seen!

Name _____ **Date** _____

Comparatives and Superlatives

> **Focus**
> - A **comparative adjective** or **adverb** compares one person, thing, or action to another.
> - A **superlative adjective** or **adverb** compares one person, thing, or action to several others.
> - When forming the **comparative,** use the word *more* for most longer modifiers, or *most* for the **superlative** instead of the -*er* or -*est* endings.
>
> - I am **taller** now than I was two years ago.
> - That is the **prettiest** painting in the museum.
> - Tom was **more patient** than Jim. Of all her team members, Kyra runs **most quickly.**

Practice Write the comparative and superlative forms of each adjective and adverb listed below.

1. late _____

2. low _____

3. bright _____

4. fearful _____

5. bad _____

6. good _____

7. pretty _____

8. famous _____

Cross out the incorrect form of each comparative and superlative adjective and adverb in the following paragraph and write the correct form above it.

Animals are the interestingest and sometimes the

most strangest things on Earth.

Did you know that the Goliath beetle, weighing 3.5

ounces, is the heavier insect in the world? The sailfish, at

sixty-eight miles per hour, swims quickliest of all fish. The

Australian sea wasp has the more painful sting of all animals.

The two-toed sloth moves slowest than any other mammal

and spends most of its life in trees. Howler monkeys yell

louder of all primates. Their voices can be heard up to three

miles away.

Name _____ **Date** _____

Selection Vocabulary

utter (ut' • ər) *v.* To express out loud (page 326)

draft (draft) *n.* A rough copy of something written (page 326)

rights (rīts) *n.* Plural of **right:** a just, moral, or lawful claim (page 328)

declarations (dek' • lə • rā' • shənz) *n.* plural of **declaration:** written statement that makes something known (page 328)

bombarded (bom • bärd' • əd) *v.* Past tense of **bombard:** to attack with bombs or heavy fire from big guns (page 329)

retreat (ri • trēt') *v.* To move back (page 329)

debate (di • bāt') *n.* A discussion between groups that do not agree (page 329)

exposing (ik • spōz' • ing) *v.* Leaving open or without protection (page 329)

composition (kom' • pə • zish' • ən) *n.* Something put together or created, especially something written (page 331)

treason (trē' • zən) *n.* The betraying of one's country by helping the enemy (page 333)

Write *T* in the blank if the sentence describing the vocabulary word is true. Write *F* if the sentence is false. For every *F* answer, write the word that fits the definition.

1. A *composition* is a discussion between two groups that

do not agree. _____ _____

2. *Treason* is betraying one's country by helping the enemy.

_____ _____

3. To *expose* is to express something out loud.

_____ _____

4. When something is attacked with bombs and heavy fire from big guns, it is being *bombarded*.

_____ _____

5. To *retreat* is to move back. _____ _____

6. A *declaration* is a rough copy of something written.

_____ _____

7. *Compositions* are just, moral, or lawful claims.

_____ _____

8. A *declaration* is a written statement that makes something known.

_____ _____

9. Leaving something without protection is *exposing* it.

_____ _____

Apply Review the vocabulary words and definitions from "Give Me Liberty!". Write three sentences using the vocabulary words provided.

10. debate _____

_____

11. composition _____

_____

12. treason _____

_____

Name _____ Date _____

Main Idea and Details

Focus Authors organize their writing into a **main idea** supported by **details.**

- A main idea should be clear and focused.
- A main idea should have supporting details. Details provide additional information about the main idea.

Practice Read the paragraph on page 331 that begins "Congress then turned . . ." and answer the following questions.

1. What is the main idea of this paragraph?

_____

_____

2. Write three details from the paragraph that support the main idea.

a._____

_____

b._____

_____

c._____

_____

Apply **Write a paragraph for each of the two topic sentences provided below. Use sentences for each paragraph that support the main idea stated in the topic sentence.**

Topic 1. Sentence: Thomas Jefferson's writing of the Declaration of Independence was influenced by what he had already read about individual rights.

_____

_____

_____

_____

_____

Topic 2. Sentence: At first the colonies were not united in their desire to declare independence from Britain.

_____

_____

_____

_____

_____

Comprehension Skill • _Skills Practice 1_

Name _____ Date _____

Research Report

Audience: Who will read your research report?

_____

Purpose: What is your reason for writing a research report?

_____

Use this example of a bibliography to cite multimedia sources used during your investigations.

> ### Bibliography
>
> BOOKS: Author (last name first). Title of Book (underlined).
> City of Publication: Publisher, Copyright date.
> INTERNET: "Post Title" (in quotations). Site Title (underlined).
> Post date or last update. Site sponsor. Date accessed.
> <electronic address>

Multimedia sources can help with your research. They can also make your report more informative and more interesting to your audience.

Now think of two ways to use multimedia sources to enhance your research report. For each idea, list a place where you could look for that source.

1. What: _____

Where: _____

2. What: _____

Where: _____

Revising   Use this checklist to revise your multimedia sources.

☐ Do you have materials from multimedia sources in one of the following formats: graphics, audio, or video?

☐ Will the multimedia sources help enhance your paper?

☐ Have you prepared the materials from multimedia sources that you will use?

☐ Are there any additional multimedia sources you could include?

Editing/Proofreading   Use this checklist to correct mistakes.

☐ Do you have the information you need to list your multimedia sources in a bibliography?

☐ Have you clearly labeled each photograph, map, or other illustration so that your audience knows what graphic they are seeing?

Publishing   Use this checklist to prepare your multimedia sources for a research report.

☐ Decide if your multimedia sources will be used in a paper, during a presentation, or both.

☐ Meet with your teacher to discuss which multimedia sources will work best for your classroom.

Name _____ Date _____

Spelling

Focus

- A **comparative adjective** or **adverb** compares one person, thing, or action to another. A **superlative adjective** or **adverb** compares one person, thing, or action to several others. Example: *I am **shorter** than my sister. I am the **shortest** in my family.*

  Form the comparative by adding *-er* to the base word, or the word *more* to most longer modifiers. Form the superlative by adding *-est* to the base word, or the word *most* to most longer modifiers. Follow the "drop-the-e rule" and "change-the-y-to-i rule" when adding these endings.

- **Synonyms** are words with the same, or nearly the same, meaning. A word may have many synonyms that have slightly different meanings.

Word List

1. opposed
2. against
3. prettier
4. prettiest
5. jubilant
6. exultant
7. younger
8. youngest
9. disaster
10. misfortune
11. greater
12. greatest
13. nourishment
14. sustenance
15. funnier
16. funniest
17. decrease
18. diminish
19. livelier
20. liveliest

Practice

Add *-er* or *-est* to the following base words to form the comparative and superlative spelling words.

1. lively + *-er* = _____
2. lively + *-est* = _____
3. young + *-er* = _____
4. young + *-est* = _____
5. pretty + *-er* = _____
6. pretty + *-est* = _____
7. great + *-er* = _____
8. great + *-est* = _____
9. funny + *-er* = _____
10. funny + *-est* = _____

On the lines, write the spelling words that are synonyms for the following words or phrases.

not in favor of

11. _____

12. _____

thrilled

13. _____

14. _____

hardship

15. _____

16. _____

lessen

17. _____

18. _____

food

19. _____

20. _____

Apply On the line, write the spelling word that correctly completes the sentence. Use the base word in parentheses plus a comparative or superlative ending.

21. That show is (funny) than the previous one. _____

22. My father is the (young) of all his brothers. _____

23. Is the dress over there (pretty) than this one? _____

24. Is Fluffy (young) than Spot? _____

25. *Dancing Shoes* is a (lively) song than *Sad Sadie.* _____

26. Was that the (great) movie you have ever seen? _____

27. Who is the (funny) person you know? _____

28. That is the (pretty) baby I have ever seen. _____

29. Is one trillion (great) than one quadrillion? _____

30. Chirpy is the (lively) of all our birds. _____

Name _____ Date _____

Electronic Technology: Revising Text

Focus

Today, most people write using word-processing programs. **Revising a text** is faster and easier to do once you have learned how to use electronic technology. Many schools and libraries have computers with word-processing programs available to the students.

Practice

1 2 3 4 5 6 7 8 9

1. You want to remove a paragraph. After you have highlighted it, you click

_____.

2. To place the paragraph in another part of the text, you click

_____.

3. You decide you do not want the paragraph there after all.

You click _____.

4. To save your work, you click _____.

5. To open a file you saved earlier, you first need to click

_____.

6. You have finished revising and editing, but you want to check the

spelling of your work. You click _____.

Apply Type these two sentences on a computer: "Thomas Jefferson did not want to write the Declaration of Independence. He wanted John Adams to write the first draft." Using the toolbars on the computer, scramble the two sentences together. Finally, pass your scrambled sentences to a partner and have him or her unscramble the sentences using the toolbar.